MYTHS
OF CREATION

PHILIP FREUND

ILLUSTRATED BY MILTON CHARLES

WASHINGTON SQUARE PRESS, INC.

New York *1965*

Acknowledgment

Since the myths in this book were first told and set down, each in its own language or dialect, perhaps in archaic Greek, Chinese, Sanskrit, Babylonian, Eskimo, or Zulu, I cannot pretend to have gathered any of them first-hand. All are from secondary sources, of course. Some of them—most, I should say—come from the famed collections of Fiske, Frazer, Frobenius, and the other mythologists, anthropologists, and psychologists whom I have mentioned at times: Bellamy, Campbell, Coomaraswamy, Fromm, Kerényi, Malinowski, and Rank. To these let me add the names of Margot Astrov, Brian Brown, Sir Peter Henry Buck, Henry Callaway, Arthur Drew, A. E. Haydon, Vera Kelsey, Leonard W. King, Hasteen Klah, S. N. Kramer, Julius Lips, J. K. Newberry, Adrian Recinos, Géza Róheim, Ruth K. Smith, and Heinrich Zimmer. I have drawn on many lesser and scattered sources, including anonymous writers.

Spelling of the names of mythological heroes tends to vary when Americanized. I have tried to keep them consistent within the limits of this book.

For the material in the chapters on scientific theories of the origin of the universe, the stars, the solar system, and the evolution of man, I owe a no less sizeable debt. Besides the specialists mentioned in the chapters, I should list books by Dr. Roy Chapman Andrews, Hal Borland, Harold Callender, Gordon Childe, Raymond D. Dart, George Eckel, Leonard Eisley, Dr. William King Gregory, Dr. William Howells, Julian Huxley, Waldemar Kaempffert, Arthur Koestler, William L. Laurence, Willy Ley, Milton

K. Munitz, Pierre Lecomte du Noüy, John J. O'Neill, John Pfeiffer, Claude Stanush, Jean Rostand; and, again, the authors of many unsigned articles.

It may be that in borrowing from so many sources, in some instances I am perpetuating errors—the writing of history has been described as an exercise wherein one researcher copies the mistakes of a predecessor—but I am hopeful that if there are any, they are no more than very small errors of detail.

*

Appreciatively to

FRANCES   WITLIN   *and*   CARL   COWL

*

CONTENTS

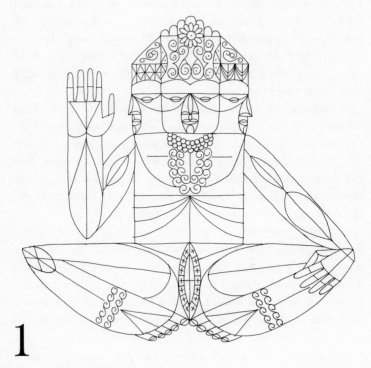

1

A GENESIS

Some thirty years ago and more, when I was enrolled at a university, I studied astronomy. One night each week I went to a little domed observatory that stood on a knoll, and afterward on cold winter nights I walked back to the campus and my dormitory room, along a path through woods beside a frozen lake. Like everyone else, I found it exciting to gaze through a telescope at the moon and the rings of Saturn. Even more thrilling was that snowy walk back from our evening class. Overhead the stars burned with frosty clarity in the winter sky and the crisp and sometimes stinging air. I was eighteen, and when I looked up at the white points of light in the dark sky, a sense of poetic wonder flooded my mind. This was very close in feeling, I'm sure, to the primitive sense of wonder of a child or savage, peering heavenward, with all the world and night about him empty and still.

An astronomy course consists of more than trips to an observatory; our professor chalked abstruse mathematics on the blackboard, and there were excursions into physics with which a youthful intelligence was hardly able to cope. But the ingenuity of astronomers greatly impressed me, as did their staggering statistics. It is not without cause that we speak of any very large figure as "astronomical."

A young man who sat alongside me in class was a good mathematician and often helped to explain the complex equations to me. He was quiet, well behaved, serious in aspect. Often we walked back together from class across the glistening, snowy campus. One day I spoke with enthusiasm and respect of the lecture we had just heard, on the origin of the solar system.

He smiled. "Yes, it's all very interesting. But of course I don't believe any of it."

"What do you mean?" Everything I was told in the classroom, I accepted without question.

"I'm a Christian. I read the Bible, and I believe what's written there."

"That God created the world in six days?"

I learned that my friend was deeply religious. He hoped to go to a theological seminary and afterward become a missionary in distant Africa. This was in the days when a religious movement called Fundamentalism was popular in America. The Fundamentalists believed in the literal interpretation of the Bible; indeed, at their urging, a science teacher named Scopes in Tennessee had been removed from his class and fined for having taught that man was descended from monkeys. The findings of science were heresies to such orthodox religionists. If my friend belonged to them, that in itself was not too startling.

But how could he sit beside me in an astronomy class and follow the blackboard demonstrations, and peer through a telescope, and yet not believe anything he heard from our professor? Every time I saw my friend taking notes on the lectures, I asked myself that. To me, his attitude was highly irrational.

At the end of the term, when we wrote our final examination, I barely won a passing grade, but my unbelieving friend—due to his mathematical skill—had the highest mark in the class.

Our professor had no inkling that his best student was a quiet skeptic. My friend's religious faith continued to puzzle me. How could anyone be exposed to the dazzling proofs of science and yet close his eyes to them?

At eighteen, I thought that the theory presented in our astronomy class was the "truth," and that my friend's belief, the Biblical one, was mere fantasy. It should have given me pause, however, that the theory propounded in college was not the one I had learned in high school, only three or four years earlier. My high school teacher had told us about the Laplace nebular hypothesis to account for the origin of the earth and the solar system; whereas now, in college, I was being given the Chamberlin-Moulton planetesimal hypothesis.

If the Laplace hypothesis was no longer scientifically sound, in what respect was it different from a "myth"?

II

It happened more recently, perhaps fifteen years ago, that I had occasion to read the Hindu *Brihadāranyaka-Upanishad* in Yeats's splendid translation. In it, I came across this vivid tale of the origin of life:

> *As a lonely man is unhappy, God was unhappy. He wanted a companion. He was as big as man and wife together; He divided Himself into two, husband and wife were born.*
>
> *God said: "Man is only half himself; his wife is the other half."*
>
> *They joined and mankind was born.*
>
> *She thought: "He shall not have me again; he has created me from himself; I will hide myself."*
>
> *She then became a cow, he became a bull; they were joined and cattle were born. She became a mare, he a stallion; she became a she-ass, he an ass; they joined and the hoofed animals were born. She became a she-goat, he a goat; she became a ewe, he a ram; they joined and goats and sheep were born. Thus He created everything down to ants, male and female.*
>
> *He put His hand into His Mouth, and there created fire as if He were churning butter. He knew that He was this creation; that He created it from Himself; that He was the cause. Who knows, finds creation joyful.*
>
> *When they say: "Sacrifice to this or that god," they talk of separate gods; but all gods are created by Him, and He is all gods.*
>
> *Whatever is liquid He created from His seed. Everything in this world is eater or eaten. The seed is food and fire is eater.*
>
> *He created the gods; created mortal men, created the immortals. Hence this creation is a miracle. He who knows, finds this miracle joyful.*

*This world was everywhere the same till name and
shape began; then one could say: "He has made such
a name and such a shape." Even today everything is
made different by name and shape.*

Later in this book, I should like to refer to that Hindu
tale and analyze it in some small measure, in the light of
what we shall have learned about the significance of myths.
We shall not be able to probe it fully, but in part, at least;
and I am certain that we shall discover something about
ourselves in so doing.

Most of us contrast in our mind only two stories of the
creation, the Biblical one and the scientific one. We assume
that one or the other is right. Either my friend the Fundamentalist had the answer, or my professor of astronomy had
it.

But it occurred to me, as I read the lively yet allegorically
profound tale in the *Brihadáranyaka-Upanishad,* that mankind provides many other stories of creation besides the
Old Testament one.

I became curious about the creation myths of other religions and races, the tales of how the world began. Whenever possible, I took note of them. I was fascinated by the
myths because of their poetic quality and accordingly collected them for my own pleasure. Of all kinds of primitive
and natural poetry, this particular myth-subject has the
most grandeur and scope and seems to be chronologically at
the very start of man's speculations.

Here is a tale of the Shilluk, a tall and stately race in the
African Sudan:

*In the beginning was Jo-Uk, the Great Creator,
and he made the Sacred White Cow. Out of the Nile
that Cow came up. The White Cow gave birth to a
man child whom she called Kola, whose grandson was
Ukwa. Ukwa took two wives, dark virgins who also*

rose out of the holy river. One of Ukwa's sons, Nyakang, a tall blue-black warrior, went south to the marshes of the Upper Nile; there he founded the Shilluk nation and became its first ret, or ruler, and a demigod. All this happened when the world was new, about four hundred years ago.

Then I came upon this story of "the beginning" recounted by an Andean race, the Aymara people of Pacajes in Bolivia:

The Snow God Kun destroyed all life on earth. Only the cruel supaya—*devils—dared to roam the thin air of the icy highlands. This happened ages and ages ago. Then the Fertility Gods, the Pacha Camaj, sent down their very own sons, the Eagle Men. They created a new race of people, to take the place of those who had been snowed under by the angry Kun. The children of the Eagle Men, the Paka-Jakes, settled on the shores of Lake Titicaca, where they are today.*

These myths sound very unlike, yet one begins to discern strange patterns in them . . . and from this a new curiosity entered my search. All the "origin" myths, though from scattered regions, have haunting similarities. How to account for that?

I think that a study of myths for their own sake would be an idle affair, a species of dilettantism, for which I have neither the time nor the temperament. What held my interest, almost from the very start, was the hint that I might learn something fundamental and permanent about the mind of man—about myself—by contemplating mythology, and especially man's always daring stories of "the beginning."

As my pleasure continued, and my hope for this quest sharpened, I finally began to think of creating a character in a novel, whose interest would parallel my own—an anthropologist who would be a collector of creation myths—and I finally did this in my philosophical romance, *The Volcano God,* which has outraged some of the more conservative critics. To prepare for the novel, my search for material became more systematic. Later I was also convinced that I should write a separate book about my findings, to develop my ideas and guesses further than the fictional form allows. I am not an anthropologist. Instead, I am a poet and novelist venturing into a special field, which, by the nature of his calling, is akin to his own. Any storyteller is something of a mythmaker.

What follows is a voyage of exploration which is serious and, in my opinion, important. I have greatly enjoyed compiling this book, because it is filled with poetry and color, articulated in some of the world's most superb allegory. Early man's gift for fantasy is astounding. One never ceases to wonder at it. And, so far as I know, this is the first time that so many creation stories have been brought together in one volume. But to share my delight in this spontaneous poetry is not my only purpose. How does man's mind work? Where can we look to find a clue more clearly than here? In these stories we can see how man reasoned when he looked at the world and first tried to explain it to himself. Let us examine his answers, his earliest and latest attempts at understanding the universe, not only in primitive myth but in recent science. In what ways do they vary? Or is man's explanation always very much the same? If there are fixed modes of thought, which have lasted since the beginning of humankind, an exciting prospect is open to us: we can learn a bit more of *how* we think, by an analysis of these creation epics, and thus further increase our store of self-knowledge.

2

FIRE AND DELUGE

According to some Australian aboriginals, Old Man Pundyil opened the door of the Sun; thereupon a stream of fire poured down upon mankind.

The Eskimos tell a similar story. At the time of the great blaze, the waters of the Arctic Ocean became so hot that they finally evaporated.

Savage man's imagination is cruelly vivid. But that re-flects—or symbolizes—the daily danger of his existence, the threat of natural accident.

The Ipurinas, a tribe in northwestern Brazil, relate that long ago the Earth was overwhelmed by a hot flood. This took place when the Sun, a caldron of boiling water, tipped over.

The Yurucaré, of Bolivia, say that Aymasuñe, the demon, was responsible for the fall of fire from heaven. Everything below died: bushes, creatures, the human race. Only one man, who had foreseen what might happen, had provided food and shelter for himself in a cave. When the fire hail began, he hid himself there. Now and then, to learn if the fire still raged, he held a long stick out of the mouth of his cave. On two occasions it came back charred, but the third time it was cool. Still cautious, however, he kept himself safe four more days before venturing out. And then, the sole survivor, he beheld a dreadful sight. The whole forest was ashes, the rivers and springs had boiled away, the very mountains were blackened.

These are not creation myths, but catastrophe myths. But they are a necessary background for the creation stories and nearly always coupled with them. They tell of a terrible fire, both cosmic and earthly.

In Hindu mythology, creation is destroyed at the end of each Kalpa, or day of Brahma, by flames belched forth from the fangs of Sesha, the serpent. Some savants have inter-preted this as referring to the appearance of a blazing comet. In the ancient Babylonian epic which describes the adventures of Gilgamesh of Erech, we learn of a fire rain spread by the Anunnaki, who rush across the heavens with their torches aloft. The Anunnaki are underworld spirits and might have escaped from spouting volcanoes.

When we leap from the Eskimos and the Yurucaré to the

Hindus and Babylonians, we are turning abruptly from savage story to highly sophisticated myth. But for our purpose at the moment that makes little difference, since we are merely stressing the universality of certain themes in all ages and places.

The Greeks have the famous fable of Phaëthon, Apollo's son, who extracted from his father a promise to let him drive the Chariot of the Sun. The youth could not hold the reins tightly enough and, zigzagging through the sky, scorching the constellations, almost destroyed our planet. Clouds vanished; Libya became a desert. The Nile, in terror, hid below the earth, where its head still is; the Ethiopians were blackened for all time. The molten landscape was changed; mountains were heated and burst into flame. Only the intervention of Zeus, toppling the unhappy Phaëthon by a well-aimed thunderbolt, saved the world from a crisped end.

Or back to savages again:

The Washo Indians, in California, have a legend about a terrible volcanic upheaval. So great was the heat of the blazing mountains that the very stars melted and fell.

In the Northern Urals, the nomadic Voguls recount the story of a holy fire flood which swept over the earth for seven years and consumed almost everything; it even charred the raft of the few men who survived. It was sent by Num Tarem, the Fatherly, as a means of destroying Xulater, the Devil. Yet this fire scourge was in vain, for the indestructible Xulater eluded it.

The catastrophe myth, then, is a universal one.

In many of the stories, the world-wide blaze is caused by man's theft of fire from the gods. Maui, of the Maoris in New Zealand, was in need of it. His old blind grandmother advised him how he could steal it from Mahu-ika, the giant who guarded the flame. Maui spoke jokingly and tricked the giant into wrestling with him. With magical words, Maui hurled Mahu-ika into the air time and again, until at last the giant fell head foremost and broke his neck. Maui quickly cut off Mahu-ika's head and seized the precious flame, but it was new to him and got away and the world began to burn. Maui and his wily old grandmother were endangered. The Fire Thief jumped into the ocean, but even the salt water was boiling. He raised his voice to Ua, the Rain God, but in vain, for the fire burned on. He pleaded with Nganga the Sleet God; with the Storm Gods Apu-hau and Apu-matangi; he sought the help of the God of Hailstorms Whatu; but none of them could prevail. The ocean was nearly gone. Only when all the gods, joining together, let all their deluges pour down at the same time, was the world fire quenched.

The Tuleyome Indians, of California, tell of Wekwek, the falcon, who stole fire but lost it from beneath his wings in flight. It set the world aflame. The Yana Indians, nearby, also have a fire-stealing myth; five men were sent to obtain the treasure, but on their way back the Coyote, who had offered to carry the fire, dropped it, and instantly it blazed around them. The rocks glowed with heat, the waters evaporated, a dense pall hung over everything, and the very existence of Earth was threatened.

The Fire Thief, indeed, is a figure shared by many races. He may be the better-known Prometheus; or he may be the Irish Prince of the Lonesome Island, who bore away a flame from the well of the Queen of Tubber Tintye. In the lore of the Hassidic Jews, too, is preserved the story of man dangerously discovering fire and letting it escape his grasp.

The myth of the world-wide blaze is often accompanied by the story of a deluge, a fearful cloudburst or sudden tidal wave, which quenches the fire; or else the deluge appears alone as the catastrophe which engulfs the Earth.

The Fire Thief is called by anthropologists the Culture Hero. If he is not the Fire Thief, the Culture Hero is the Deluge Survivor. When all others perish, this Hero escapes. The best-known Deluge Survivor is Noah, but mythology is filled with hundreds of other figures like him.

Nichant, the hero of the Gros Ventres, swims while holding onto a buffalo horn. Rock, the bold ancestor of the Arapaho Indians, fashions himself a boat of fungi and spiderwebs. The lone progenitor of the Annamese saves himself in a tom-tom. The hero of the Ahoms in Burma uses a gigantic gourd which, by magical intervention, providentially grows out of a little seed. Trow, of the Tringus Dyaks of Borneo, is tossed on the waters in a trough; as is the heroine of the Toradjas of Celebes, though hers is— most unromantically—a swill trough. The ancestors of the Chané of Bolivia find refuge in an earthenware pot that floats.

One compilation shows that there are over five hundred deluge myths, belonging to over two hundred and fifty peoples or tribes. The Cashinaua of Western Brazil tell of a great flood, as do the Makusi of British Guiana and the Caribs of Central America. When a dove brought back a willow twig, the Mandan Indians of Dakota learned that the inundation was subsiding.

Other North American tribes as far apart as the Salinan and Chimariko Indians of California and the Crees of Manitoba and the Shawnees of Florida have similar stories. So do the Hurons, north of Lake Ontario, and the Algonquins along the St. Lawrence.

In Europe and the Near East, the flood myth is the same. The Lithuanians are saved in a nutshell, which Pramzimas has eaten in heaven and thrown down to give his "offspring," one man and one woman, a chance to escape. Num Tarem spares the Voguls by building them an ark, an iron ship, with a roof of sevenfold sturgeon skin. The Greeks tell of three great floods: Zeus destroys the Race of Bronze by a deluge which only Deukalion and his wife Pyrrha survive. Finally, when the waste of waters lessens, their ark comes to rest on Mount Parnassus. With them, mankind begins its history once more. Other Greek saviors and refugees from floods are Ogygos and Dardanos. The Babylonian deluge story is clearly a prototype of the Hebrew one: Like Noah, Utnapishtim has an ark and releases from it a raven and a dove, to discover if the invading waters have gone.

The Culture Hero, thus, is the founder of the tribe, or perhaps of a new race. He alone—or with a small group of lesser companions—has been saved from the catastrophe by his daring resourcefulness, or because he has been singled out by the gods' favor.

He also brings with him from an earlier era, before the world-wide disaster, the supremely important secret of fire. He remembers how things were on Earth "before." He is the sole inheritor of human knowledge, all that the race has learned through preceding aeons. He seems almost to have come to the Earth from the sky or moon. His appearance to a few huddled tribes in places of refuge, perhaps on a dry mountain top, coincides with or occurs soon after a time of fire and molten rock and clouds of suffocating ash—volcanic outpourings, followed by tidal waves caused by earthquakes—and so he might be blamed for having brought it on by his great boldness or *hubris*, as are such culture heroes as Maui and Wekwek and the Coyote. But carrying knowledge from the past he is also a light-bringer, a savior, and this too accounts for his identification as the Fire Thief. He has stolen fire from the sky and given it to man.

At night there are shining lights in the vault of heaven; what is more logical than to suppose that fire has originated there?

The moon is the brightest of all objects in the dark sky. The Tolowas say that following a vast flood, only one couple is left on Earth's highest peak. They shiver in the cold, but the Indians who live in the moon above them have fire aplenty. From the moon, then, a firebrand is brought down.

To the Loucheaux, at the time of a deluge, a godlike man comes from the moon, and later returns there again. Endless numbers of myths relate the adventures of such visitors from the moon. Some stay here; some later go back to their home in the far air.

Fire Thief, Deluge Survivor. The Hero has a third role: he is the Dragon Slayer. The god Indra, the Hebrew angel Michael, and the gods Thraeton, Marduk, and Ra of Persia, Babylonia, and Egypt, and the Greek warrior Cadmus, are all killers of the fabulous beast. So is Siegfried, in the lore of the Teutons; and Beowulf, and Thor. The legends of most races tell of battles between a fearless champion of mankind and a scaly fire-breathing monster. In this suspenseful fight, the Hero has need of a magic weapon, and is miraculously armed. It is amazing how often this incident occurs in world myth; it is found in Celtic stories, the tales of Indonesia.

As universal history unfolds in myth, the Hero takes on a final role and becomes a prophet and instructor. The Bogotá Indians of Colombia report a flood. When it ebbs, Zuhé—a tall, bearded divine messenger—appears from the East. He teaches the stricken people how to till the soil once more, to weave clothes, and to carve altars and honor their gods. The Babylonians speak of Oannes, who comes out of the sea, shining and scaled like a fish. He finds a people who live like beasts. He shows them how to build towns and fair temples, and how to make use of the land, to have it bear them sustaining fruits. Six other heavenly beings follow him with instructive messages for mankind.

The Culture Hero may once have been human, an actual survivor of a catastrophe, or an early and benignly wise leader. Or he might be an idealized projection, a composite figure. As tribal history dissolves into myth or is elaborated by it, he is slowly raised to the rank of demigod. Sometimes he rises to the very top of the hierarchy of gods; he may end his steady process of deification—or enskyment—as the ruling god himself; as, indeed, the creation deity. Osiris, beginning as a Culture Hero, becomes the most loved of Egyptian divinities. The saintly young Indian prince, Gautama, is similarly elevated. So is the Teutonic chieftain, Odin.

Although not all Culture Heroes attain that apotheosis, they are a brilliant company. Chon is the Hero of the Peruvians. Quetzalcoatl and Tezcatlipoca, of the Mexicans. Votan, of the Mayas. Raven, of the Eskimos. Kut-o-yis, of the Blackfoot Indians; and Manzabozho, of the Algonquins; and Water Jar Boy, of the Pueblo Indians. Fu Hsi, Shen Nung, and Huang Ti, of the Chinese. Trow is celebrated by the folklore of Borneo. Besides Prometheus and Deukalion, the Greeks have Palamedes and Cecrops. The Romans, cunning and defiant Aeneas. Finnish myth lauds Väinämöinen and Lemminkainen. The Yakuts, of Siberia, recount the exploits of The White Youth. Finn MacCool and Cuchulainn enliven Irish legendry with their magical deeds. The chivalric and generous acts of King Arthur are recalled by the Welsh and the English. Maui, Siegfried, Muchukunda, Oisin. Gilgamesh, Hotu Matua. Each of these, in his biography, illustrates some aspect if not all the details of the same reiterated theme, and frequently his story combines a very large number of them.

Interesting efforts have been made to draw a psychological profile of this popular and ever-shining figure who later becomes a god or, at least, a human being of intermittent supernatural powers. Perhaps the most rewarding of these is Otto Rank's *The Myth of the Birth of the Hero* (recently republished in a collection of Rank's essays which I have edited). Others are J. K. Newberry's *The Rainbow Bridge* and Joseph Campbell's *The Hero with a Thousand Faces*. Rank notes how the Hero's birth is always remarkable: he is immaculately conceived, like Väinämöinen and Gautama; or, if not that, like Moses and Oedipus a changeling of royal lineage; and Campbell outlines the many metamorphoses the Hero tends to undergo and the striking likeness of his trials, whatever the racial origin of the myth. Another portrait of the soul or psyche of the Hero is to be found in Toynbee's *A Study of History*. In these books—Newberry's, Campbell's, and Toynbee's—we also see some Heroes assume the character of Divine Scapegoats and transcend their first shape or personality to become compassionate World Redeemers.

What explanation can be put forth for the similarity of these catastrophe myths of fire and deluge, for the likeness of these Culture Heroes, in every quarter of the globe? As I have already observed, we shall find the same similarity when we come to look at the several categories of creation myths.

When I sought an answer to this, I came upon a sharp controversy as to how myths are to be interpreted. The opposed theories are almost as interesting as the myths themselves.

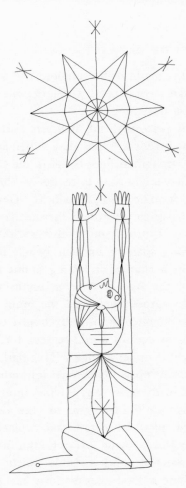

3

THE INTERPRETATION
OF MYTH

For thousands of years, the leading myths were taken
to be instances of divine revelation. To question them
imperiled not only man's soul but his life, exposing him to
a charge of heresy. In any event, a pious Hindu would not

have doubted the myths of his religion; nor would a devout Jew or Christian have expressed skepticism concerning the Biblical creation story.

A good many persons in the Western world, in our century, still hold this view. What they will read in my book might possibly strengthen their belief in the Old Testament story, though they might have to revise—or "broaden"—their conception of it. The Old Testament "Genesis" is very likely a more complex story than they realize. Yet nothing in my essay need disturb anyone's other-worldly faith.

After that long span of implicit belief, the eighteenth century brought a change of feeling about myth. To the philosophers of the Age of Reason, myths were barbaric superstitions that grossly befogged the mind of man. The Age of Enlightenment optimistically hoped to sweep them all away. Then the cosmos would be seen for what the new scientists thought it to be: a huge self-regulating mechanism that somehow continues to operate interminably by perpetual motion, with never any divine intervention. The goal of the eager *Philosophes* was to take away from religion its specific pictorial detail and replace the Bible's radiant imagery with a vague sort of theism in which God is a pure and intangible and invisible Spirit. Without the help of myth, indeed, God loses his form and personality in the human mind. The world is real, and God is undefined.

In the late nineteenth century there was an artistic revolt against so much materialism and mechanism in philosophy, and the beauty of myth was rediscovered. At first this was merely praise and a new respect for myth as a form of folk poetry. But soon the Romantic artists of that century delved deeper and claimed to find in myth the origin of art, religion, and history. At the same time, myths were revived in the most advanced religious thinking. But now they were looked upon not as literal facts but as allegories of profound meaning, age-old and probably adumbrant of the divine. In still another sphere of the Age of Romanticism, the political worth of myths as "cultural tradition" was exalted by nationalists and racists. Wagner, in his exceedingly lengthy operas, uses Teutonic legendry after this fashion. In all this, however, one senses an element of the patronizing on the part of delighted or amused intellectuals, toward whatever is naïve or simple and primitive.

Finally, in the realm of science, scholars of the late nineteenth and early twentieth century began to develop some daring new ideas about myth, which I shall try to summarize in the next few paragraphs.

The Myth as Art and Philosophy

Are myths only examples of early man's imagination freely at play? Sometimes, when reading the absurdly pretentious claims made about these tales, we are tempted to dismiss them as that and nothing more. Undoubtedly, they are examples of the first storytellers' fantasies. We picture the huddled Cro-Magnon huntsmen as the shadows of night expand in the craggy Pyrenees, or Ipiutak men near the Arctic Circle, or the crouched jungle warriors in a ring about their smoky village fires, listening with awe and eager credulity to the narratives of their tribal chronicler and poet. We can well believe that the taleteller delighted himself by adding new details to a hoary account of a past chieftain's prowess in combat, or a wondrous celestial event, a comet flashing across the sky or a meteor falling; his fancy inventing endlessly, to startle his hearers and hold their interest. His stories, developing over thousands of years, attain the quality of great fiction; they are cumulative works of art.

But very few scholars who compare the tales and study them think them only prompted by idle fancy. It becomes immediately apparent that, consciously or unconsciously, the stories about Wekwek and Hotu Matua have been told with a more serious purpose; the authors preach morals and hand on instruction. They are philosophers and teachers. Yet they never fail to be creators of enthralling fiction.

The Myth as Primitive Science

For a long time, myth interpretation was dominated by the so-called Naturalistic School, to which belonged Andrew Lang and Thomas Carlyle. Especially popular in the nineteenth century, it held that myths are a form of primitive science, filled with early man's ingenious efforts to account for the bewildering and threatening world about him. As he sought to do this, savage man was moved to people the objects around him with spirits and demons. He could not imagine those visible and invisible objects—trees, rocks, clouds, stars, and wind—as truly different from himself. Aware of his inner life, both a waking and dreaming consciousness, he logically supposed all other forms of plant and animal life and natural phenomena to have souls and personalities, too.

Every tree conceals a dryad, and every grove or spring has its protective deity; every mountain, above the maw of the smoking volcano, its god; the river has its troupe of nymphs, and the rocks of the rapids and seashore their sirens; and thunder in the rainstorm is the voice of a greater god who can punish man with fierce lightning bolts. Natural forces behave as human beings themselves might.

A man must treat all of nature with fearful respect. His own feelings are matched by those invisible beings who dwell on every side around him: the ocean grows angry and jealously swamps his fishing boat, for some good reason; the offended wind screams and strikes back and desolates his village, in reply to some transgression; or the pleased earth confers its blessing at harvesttime, to repay him for some ungrudging sacrifice.

From this picture of the world grow man's earliest attempts at magic. He seeks to influence the threatening demons and spirits and demigods by imitating or propitiating them; and this repeated attempt at magic gives birth to ritual, to which myth is probably closely related.

The Moon and the Sun

The presupposition of the Naturalistic School, touched on above, is that we find in myth a naïve form of science. Especially prevalent in Germany, however, is the idea that myths do not seek to explain every phase of the physical world. Instead, only a single aspect of it is chosen. Many German schools, among them Ehrenreich, Siecke, and Winckler, say that ultimately all myths refer to the moon. The circling of that silvery orb always commanded the awe of savage man. Early man's religion is narrowed by these scholars to his moon worship or moon wonder. Tides, menstruation, and phases of light for the harvest seemingly occur at the moon's behest. Ancient calendars are soon fixed by it. We have already noticed how the Culture Hero of the Loucheaux is a godlike man who comes from there and later returns to it, and how the ancestors of the Tolowas obtain a firebrand from Indians living up there. In Brazil, the Tupis still propound that the moon, to them the personification of all evil, falls periodically on the Earth and wreaks havoc on it. A famous South Rhodesian creation tale has to do with the Moon Man. Certainly there is no lack of myths about the moon.

Controversy has long gone on between the Lunar School and the Solar School, however. Leo Frobenius has travelled far in Africa and the South Seas gathering tales that bear out his contention that myths have nearly always been inspired by the sun, the most dazzling source of light and heat. Frobenius has an impressive list to bear him out, too, and maintains that at the heart of every myth—whether or not the primal sun is overtly spoken of—it has been metaphorically intended.

Another school with a similar point of view is the Meteorological. Müller and Kuhn believe that it is man's attention to the colors of the sky, the wind, the changing weather of the heavens, which is largely reflected in myth. John Fiske, the American historian and philosopher, emphasizes that the ruling god in every pantheon has been the sky deity. Like many other mythologists, Fiske relies on philology, word origins, to substantiate this; he delves into Sanskrit, particularly. He identifies the Greek myths as deriving from Indian ones, and then shows—by the similarity of Sanskrit and Greek names—that Zeus is "the sky" and Athena, born from his forehead, is "the light of day." Helen is the fickle twilight.

Man must look up to the sky; he feels ever smaller when contemplating and exploring its infinite height above him. Bertrand Russell is led by consideration of this to describe religion, somewhat disdainfully, as a kind of heliotropism. Man's thoughts are drawn not only toward the sky, but most of all toward its fiery center, the sun; and his poetic imagination is enkindled by it. (The sense of this does not strike me as anything that disparages the religious impulse.)

It is a well-sustained theory that man's image of God is invariably associated with a skyey brightness, as in the religion of the Incas and the ancient Iranians, the fire-worshipping Zoroastrians; and the Jews, whose Yahweh is enthroned in blazing light; and the Greeks and Roman Stoics.

An interesting effort to trace the history of some esoteric aspects of this thesis will be found in a little book called *Phos,* by Gillis Wetter.

The Myth as Literal History

Quite opposed to this Naturalistic School is the Historical. Myths are factual accounts of the world's past, chronicles of long-ago happenings.

The foremost advocate of this point of view is Dr. W. H. Rivers. Among others is Hans Bellamy, who in *Moons, Myths, and Man* says: "Myths are not the work of imagination, but the result of interpreted observation. In them a great store of ancient and direct experience is laid up. They are fossil history: actual happenings which lie far beyond the reach of history proper. Generally, of course, they are clumsily and quaintly described, but always with simplicity and candor; and the reports are almost without exception literally true." In Bellamy's opinion, myths go much further back in man's past than any known human fossils. "Before man could write, his memory must have been very remarkable. Myths have been carried untold centuries—perhaps 'thousands of centuries.' The static character of early historical, and therefore also of prehistoric culture, would be very instrumental in this. It is the introduction of artificial memories, of books, that has given us a wrong idea of the storing and recording power of the human brain; it is the use of writing that has destroyed much of this most primitive and important capacity of man."

After the myth, says Bellamy, comes the allegory, in which man's aesthetic sense is at work reading a meaning—usually a religious one—into the factual report, which has become a legend. But essentially the myth is based on a real occurrence, probably of fathomless antiquity.

We can, indeed, best account for the fire and deluge stories by accepting some such hypothesis. Sometime, in the world's remote past, great fires and floods harassed our ancestors. Was it a single immense catastrophe, or do the flood tales refer to many local disasters, such as might have befallen any tribe anywhere, allowing for the vast span of years which has elapsed since the "beginning"? Or the myths may spring from a time when earth was still cooling and volcanoes leapt up everywhere, and lava spread and ran from Pacific islands and other coastal areas into huge, surging seas. Smoke and gas in the sky would bring on torrential rains, prolonged storms. We can ask ourselves what else inspired so many tales of a cataclysmic landscape.

Other scholars speculate, however, that it might have been a cosmic event which these universal legends reflect, such as the earth's capture of the moon. The waters suddenly raised by its first gravitational pull might have overflowed into the coastal lands. The Culture Heroes were really the sheerly fortunate or bravely resolute survivors of that time. The moon's capture, too, might have resulted in a change of speed of the earth's rotation, which could have dire effects.

Still another possibility is that the fire myths were suggested by the explosion of a supernova. Such new stars, the "red giants," have periodic pulsations of luminosity. The Milky Way galaxy has seen three flare-ups of supernovae, all well documented, during the past thousand years. One extraordinarily brilliant explosion, recorded by the Chinese in the eleventh century, lasted for a month and was clearly visible even by day. At night, it was ten times brighter than the moon, and hence a blinding object. The debris of it is now to be observed in the Crab nebula. In the sixteenth century, Tycho's star acted similarly, as did thirty years later Kepler's supernova, which at its source had an intensity of heat and brightness twenty-five times that of the sun. If our own sun were to behave that way, the side of earth facing it would be crisped black in a bare thirty minutes. Within a few days, after the oceans vanished in live steam, our whole planet would be mere vapor. In the early days of the solar system, when the sun was a billion or two billion years younger, something just a little like that could have occurred.

All these hypotheses, and a few more, are somewhat plausible. A number of others have been added to them, however, by the pseudo scientists who have always been attracted to the fanciful realm of myth to lend credence to otherwise flimsy physical theories. Such a one is the claim that the earth, rotating on its axis, has several times wobbled and turned over, thus reversing the positions of the North and South poles. Supposedly this has happened because the weight of the polar icecaps has grown too heavy and upset the planet's balance; like a spinning top, it has lost momentum and toppled over. The immediate consequence would be a change of climate on earth; temperate regions would quickly become scorching deserts or vast bright ice fields; huge tidal waves would drown low-lying coastal areas; and, in dramatic fashion, other terrestrial upheavals would take place. The proponents of this theory deem it not only historic but prophetic, for they think that unless we break up the present icecaps by atomic bombing, the same overturn will surely occur again.

Along with these historians and prophets of disaster must be put those who talk of probable collisions between earth and a comet at some past or future time; or of a hurtling together of our world and an asteroid or meteor of immense size; or the coming together of our sun with another star. Any such impact would have horrific results on our planet, and these "scholars" claim that the fire-and-deluge myths bear them out. Widely read a decade ago was a book by Immanuel Velikovsky, *Worlds in Collision,* which typically purported to substantiate Biblical stories by reference to such a celestial crash. But physical science and proper mythology hardly support Velikovsky's far-fetched conclusions.

Oddly enough, Bellamy himself subscribes to a theory almost as discredited: that of Hans Hoerbiger, a Viennese machine-builder, who argues that earth had earlier moons than the present one. They were ice coated, and the earth's gravitational pull, or the satellites' own altered speed of rotation after their capture, broke the lunar ice coats into floating blocks, heated the water beneath them into clouds of steam, until moon after moon, of perhaps six in all, disintegrated and fell into earth's atmosphere, like flaming comets, again causing tidal waves and volcanic disturbances here below. Hoerbiger calls this the Cosmic Ice Theory, and Bellamy has gathered hundreds of myths to help prove it. He cites all those that tell of the moon exploding or falling from the sky, of fire coming from the moon; or the lunar origin of hailstorms, earthquakes, deluges.

Bellamy describes early man as the intelligent spectator of these successive cataclysms, from mountaintops and other places of refuge. The moon, perhaps, was much closer to earth then and brighter than the sun, and so might have been spoken of as the sun. This allows Bellamy, very ingeniously, to appropriate all sun myths as moon myths, and thereby document his case still more impressively. He even goes so far as to equate Hoerbiger's disintegrating moons to "serpents" in the sky; he believes that the widespread myth of the Culture Hero as a dragon slayer originates from that resemblance: the captured moons would have trailing tails of light. The Persians, says Bellamy, referred to a fiery dragon which rose in the south and covered the entire zodiac with its tail; the Hindus relate how fire issues from the mouth of the serpent Sesha. Chinese legendry gives us a fiery reptile, a thousand miles long, who creates bright light by opening his innumerable eyes. He is also the cause of wind and storms. The Indians speak of the Milky Way as "the Path of the Serpent." In the Icelandic *Edda,* the serpent Jormungand is the "Earth Spanner." Bellamy asks whether the Jews' Satan is not really derived from *shaitan*, "to make water," suggesting the moon's blame for the floods. What were the missiles hurled by the Titans and their foes in the heavenly battles pictured by Hesiod, the Greek? The "droppings or excrements of abominable dragons"? To all races, the cosmic enemy appears in the same form: a fire-breathing monster. The Culture Hero is the symbolic victor over them. So goes Bellamy's amazing book.

A more likely explanation of the dragon-slaying story might be that earthly "dragons," the beasts he feared, were man's natural enemies. They became a symbol of evil, yes; prehistoric man must actually have fought with them, and might have chosen to identify any celestial menace with them.

The Historical School does not exhaust its many theories with this. The universality of certain myths could have come about by their having been spread by the migrations of people across both great oceans, the Atlantic and Pacific, from a common point of origin. Or there might once have been land bridges between the now widely separate continents and major islands. Else, perhaps, there were formerly vast colonial powers in prehistoric times, and the tales were disseminated from one center as later were the Jewish-Christian ones, through opportune conquests. The most repeated story is that of a lost continent and empire, Atlantis, which might have existed west of the Straits of Gibraltar and shores of Africa. Many of the myths, supposedly, refer to events which occurred there. Oceanographers tell us, however, that the sea bed shows no signs of a lost continent anywhere. This does not discourage the dream of Atlantis, which goes back to Plato.

The interpretation of myth as literal history might

promise to be the most sober approach of all, but more often as we have seen it has led to imaginative excesses. Yet that does not deny a factual content in some myths, though obviously it is hard to establish what proportion of truth should now be attributed to them. In a very recent German book, *Man, God, and Magic,* by Ivar Lissner, claims for the historicity of myth are put forth once again and formidably argued. The religious beliefs of primitive peoples scattered in remnants all over the globe are descended from prehistory all the way back to Peking Man, says Lissner. Such primitive peoples, in their ideas of God and Creation, remember an actual event passed from one generation to another by word of mouth. Like Bellamy, Lissner asserts that man, becoming civilized and divorced from his natural environment, has only done so at the cost of dulling his powers of memory and intuition.

Frazer: *Myth and Ritual*

One of the most famous of modern anthropologists was Sir James Frazer. After three-quarters of a century, some of Frazer's data in his celebrated study *The Golden Bough* has been called into question. But his popular influence is still immense, and his generalizations are still widely respected.

Frazer shares Andrew Lang's belief that myth began as a form of primitive science, but his theory goes somewhat beyond that. He suggests that some myths are *belated* rather than initial explanations, not of natural objects or processes, but of long-honored magical rites.

Savage man peoples his environment with spirits and demons and seeks to control them by a ritual consisting of imitation or propitiation. Frazer reports on the Cambodian hunter who, naked, approaches his own nets, falls into them, cries, "Look, I'm caught!" in order to work a charm on game beasts to do likewise. *The Golden Bough* also tells of the Ojibways who shoot burning arrows during an eclipse of the sun, to rekindle its light; and of the Zulus who, to make rain, kill a "heaven bird" and throw it into a pool: the heavens wail for the loss and weep.

Some of the imitative acts listed by Frazer are far more complicated, however; it is hard to grasp their present intention. When such a rite has outlived its original purpose, and its true meaning is obscure, a myth might be needed to justify its continuance. The magical practice has become too well established to be discarded, and the myth provides a new *why* for it.

On a more sophisticated level, a popular rite is reinterpreted in a later age to suit a new theology, as Christianity took over many heathen rituals and festivals and, Frazer says, provided fresh stories to lend them a more modern significance.

The Golden Bough is a pursuit of only one mythical theme, that of the dying and resurrected god, the Divine Scapegoat, who is also the vegetation deity. Frazer cites examples of this motif for several thousand pages. He traces it not only through the tales and customs of savage societies scattered everywhere on four continents, but also in the peasant folklore of contemporary Europe.

Frazer gives us, thus, another instance of the astonishing likeness of myth everywhere. He ventures his view that we need not assume that Western peoples borrowed this concept, of the dying and reborn god or savior, from the older societies of the Orient and primitive man. "More probably the resemblance which may be traced in this respect between the religions of the East and West is no more than what we commonly, though incorrectly, call a fortuitous coincidence, the effect of similar causes acting alike on the similar constitution of the human mind in different countries and under different skies."

Is the whole question of the similarity of myth subject as simple as Frazer supposes?

Freud: *Myth and Inhibitions*

Sigmund Freud was inevitably attracted to mythology. (He admitted that Frazer's work was one of his chief inspirations.) But Freud thought it needful to delve much deeper into the material of these tales. He was soon struck by the resemblance between myth and dream. In myth, as in dream, dramatic events take place free of the bounds of time and space. The Hero undergoes miraculous transformations: from one sex to another, as with Krishna; from life to death to triumphant birth again, as with Osiris and Dionysus; and he experiences unceasing frustrations. He also performs bold deeds, which might be compensatory wish fulfillments on the part of the storyteller, who in turn gives voice to the reveries of Everyman.

Eventually, Freud describes myth as primitive man's attempt upon waking to make a coherent whole of the incoherent materials of his terribly vivid dreams. When we scan the universal body of myth, we do find it crowded with symbols that are now called "Freudian." The Culture Hero battles with horrendous monsters—that is the story of Marduk and Cadmus and Siegfried. The.Hero takes refuge in the bellies of fish—that is the history of Perseus and Jonah and the Eskimos' Raven. The Hero journeys across water and commits flagrant acts of sodomy or incest. Other symbolic deeds, such as the fire theft, are also susceptible of a Freudian reading, for they could have a clear sexual import.

Freud asserts that these are the persistent reveries of the race. In mankind's myths, the repressed desires of primitive people are set free; not least amongst them, as has been pointed out, the Oedipal impulse. Or the guilty wishes are disguised and censored in their mythical formulation, as Freud claims often happens in our dreams, too. The myth is to be read and probed just as the dream is, a task to which the psychoanalyst brings his whole apparatus of dream interpretation. For example, what Phaëthon seeks in his long quest for Apollo is atonement with his unknown father; and the same is true of the Twin Warriors of the Navaho who also undergo many ordeals in search for their parent, the Sun, who fiercely denies begetting them, until with magical help they prove their true right to kinship.

I can cover but the barest outline of Freud's involved theory as he outlines it in his *Totem and Taboo*. Freud finds children, savages, and neurotics to be very much alike in their imaginative life. All are animists and have what Freud calls "archaic constitutions." We can best understand primitive men by studying our own children, suggests Freud, and we can best understand modern neurotics by observing fear-ridden savages. Neurotics and paranoiacs repeat in intense form the psychic processes of primitive folk. Like early mythmakers, today's mentally ill persons try to form systems to offset the confusion of their dreams and fears, which in the savage are also a touch paranoiac. There is a close connection between the power of the taboo and the compulsion neurosis. The magical rite, which is often bound to a primitive taboo, is like the obsessive act of a compulsive neurotic. It represents, too, gratification through hallucination or fantasy, as in the child's imitative play. Comprehension of all this must underlie, says Freud, Frazer's more factual and superficial examination of a magical rite and its related myth.

Freud is deeply convinced that sometime very early in human history the Oedipal drama first took place: brutal sons killed their fathers (the Primal Father) in a jealous struggle for possession of their mothers, and this original crime has left its mark on mankind's conscience ever since; it is responsible for our feeling, basic because inherent, of "original sin." Perhaps this was a single crime, forever remembered, though unconsciously; or perhaps it was a re-enacted one, often brought on by rivalry between sons and fathers in the prehistoric horde. It has since found expression in rites of sacrifice and reconciliation with God the Father, who was later conceived in the image of the Primal Father of the cave man. Freud believes that "the beginnings of religion, ethics, society, and art meet in the Oedipus complex." He puts it another way: "In the beginning was the deed," the murder of the father by his son. This momentous crime echoes through the tales of primitive men.

Certainly, Freud's is a valuable and stimulating contribution to our thinking about myth. His disciples have elaborated upon his premises, many of them in ways slightly their own, and an extensive psychoanalytic literature about myth has resulted. Some persons will hold back from a full acceptance of it; they will welcome some Freudian explanations as likely, and others as farfetched, to say the least. A growing number of persons have begun to look upon Freudianism as only another pseudo science. Or else, like the late Professor Malinowski, they may question the authority of psychoanalysis to speak in this particular realm. Malinowski asked: "What did Freud really know about savages? He never lived with them."

Malinowski: *Myth is Pragmatic*

Another noted anthropologist of our time has been Bronislav Malinowski, also an admirer of Frazer. Malinowski did live with savages, the childlike Trobriand Islanders in the Pacific. In his subsequent lectures and writings, he dismissed much of Freud's theorizing as nonsense. If the psychoanalysts had actually visited a primitive society to observe the role of myth there, they would have very different ideas about it. Freud and his followers, Malinowski implies, carried out all their research in libraries.

Malinowski states that the socially pragmatic role of the myths is the only important one. The tales are of three kinds: stories told about the village fires or in the thatched huts for *amusement;* legends which constitute *tribal history;* and, finally, *sacred myths.* These are not considered symbolic by the half-naked savages but are accepted as facts. The sacred myths are not even primitive science, for the loinclothed aborigines lack the instinct to question and have little ability to think abstractly; their thought processes are too concrete. Instead, the stories are endlessly repeated only to enforce ancient tribal customs, particularly economic ones; or to establish the prestige of ruling clans or families; or, perhaps, to fill gaps or cover up inconsistencies in the so-called historical legends. But the myths have no deep psychological meaning, and no real value as records.

In *Myth in Primitive Psychology,* Malinowski says: "The myth in a primitive society, that is, in its original living form, is not a mere tale told but a reality lived. It is not in the nature of an invention such as we read in our novels today, but living reality, believed to have occurred in primordial times and to be influencing ever afterward the world and the destinies of men. . . . These stories are not kept alive by vain curiosity, neither as tales that have been invented nor again as tales that are true. For the natives on the contrary they are the assertion of an original, greater, and more important reality through which the present life, fate, and work of mankind are governed, and the knowledge of which provides men on the one hand with motives for ritual and moral acts, on the other with directions for their performance."

Malinowski would seem to agree with Emile Durkheim.

Myth is one agency for shaping the individual to the culture of his group, for myth is filled with allegorical instruction: in it are the beliefs of the community, which each member is called upon to share, with a consequent lasting effect on his behavior.

A Reconsideration of Malinowski

When some of my readers come upon Malinowski's words, they may feel the passage of a cool wind of common sense through much of what has been written about mythology. Any such testimony from an eminent anthropologist who has actually spent much time with savages is bound to be impressive. Indeed, Professor Malinowski's view negates much that I would like to discuss later in this book.

I am encouraged to go ahead, though, because I believe that one can quickly find contradictions and inadequacies in what Malinowski says.

What of the tales which Malinowski himself gathered in the Trobriand Islands? As we shall see, they very definitely do "explain" or offer a reply to a prescientific sense of wonder. Someone must have asked very pertinent questions, in an earlier day. Belief in "an original, greater, and more important reality through which the present life, fate, and work of mankind are governed"—to use Malinowski's own phrase—certainly calls for a degree of abstract thought on the part of both the mind that has been curious enough to inquire and the mind that invents the tale by way of a reply. What Malinowski does not account for is where these stories came from, who first composed them.

Why are fantastic precedents for present practices offered by the tribal storytellers? What supposedly happened in the past is set up as a sanction for a continuing ideal, in order to assure its perpetuation. The Hungarian mythologist, Kerényi, points out that a myth does make things clear to the otherwise bewildered savage, though without straining the believer's mind, because the mythical answers are allowed to go unchallenged. Thus, as Malinowski claims, a myth, having become tribal dogma, does not "explain" because the hearer is simply not permitted to doubt it; the story is to be accepted as factual, not symbolical, and no longer to be explored intellectually. But originally a scale of values was expressed by it, and those values might well have included expression of unconscious desires as well as conscious ones. Otherwise the stories might never have taken the shape they did, or have gained their popular acceptance.

Malinowski describes the role of myth amongst certain South Sea islanders today. He fails to make a distinction between them and their ancestors, from whom the ancient tales have been handed down. His assumption here is that contemporary savages are very like their progenitors, but this is widely open to question. The culture of a primitive people is largely static, yet the passage of many thousand years has doubtless resulted in many changes in detail, however constant man's mode of thinking remains on the whole. Similarly, savages today do not live in simple societies; their cultures are very complex, often enigmatically so, and are the accretion of long tribal or communal experience. When Malinowski complains that Freud has not spent time with "savages," he is perhaps not making a pointed criticism. Freud could not go back and live in the prehistoric times about which he was speculating; nor did Malinowski.

Finally, we must recall that the culture studied by Malinowski in the Trobriand Islands, for instance, is that of a people exceptionally backward and naïve. He describes them as a group so dull-witted that they could not associate the sexual act and paternity, so that children have no known "fathers" amongst them; instead, the head of the family is the uncle, the mother's brother. Even their legends are comparatively crude. The major myths in other parts of the world are those of peoples of a far higher level of intelligence. Obviously the Sumerians and pre-Homeric Greeks were far superior to today's South Sea island savages. Contemporary tribes in South American jungles or on islands in the Melanesian archipelago do give us clues to the nature of earlier man, but we cannot draw fixed conclusions from them. They are clearly inferior examples of mankind; that is one reason history has passed them by.

I think we must always keep sight, however, of the functional role of myth, a concept which Malinowski took from Frazer and richly developed.

Vico

Malinowski, as well as other social psychologists and anthropologists of note such as Hubert and Mauss and Crawley, had an important predecessor to whom tribute should be paid: Giovanni Battista Vico.

Two hundred and fifty years ago, Vico saw that history could be studied through mythology. He spoke of it as a semipoetical expression of the social structures of the peoples who had conceived the stories. He said that in myth a primitive and imaginative mind presents to itself what a more reflective mind would formulate in codes of law and morality.

Vico also urged a study of modern savages, since they have a mentality akin to ancient ones. He anticipated Freud, too, by describing children as savages of a kind, and recommended looking more deeply into children's fairy tales, which modern psychologists have been doing with surprising results. If we are now told by mythologists that in the childish jingle of "London Bridge is falling down" there is an echo of a dark and terrible rite of human sacrifice, or if a psychoanalyst finds the tale of "Little Red Riding Hood" filled with sexual symbolism, we can trace the inspiration for this back, for good or ill, to the fertile hints of Vico. In him, Frazer, Freud, and Malinowski had a shrewd precursor.

Outlined in this chapter are the basic schools of myth interpretation, and there are others which we shall examine later.

4

THE WATERY BIRTH

With only a few exceptions, the creation myths describe a "beginningless God" whose wish summons the universe into being. The myths tell how this was accomplished, by what magic, and what has happened to people in the world since then. But the first storytellers seldom ask whence came the Creator Himself. God, regardless of the name or form given him, already rules the void. He broods over the stormy darkness, as in our own *Genesis*.

But early man's concept of God was also limited. God was not always thought of as immortal. Frazer tells us that, according to the first Greeks, Zeus died and was buried in Crete. His grave was shown on that rocky island, as was that of his son Dionysus at Delphi. Another of Zeus's sons, the brightest one, Apollo, died too. Frazer informs us that other primitive peoples still think the same way. Some North American Indians declare that the Great Spirit who made the world must have died long ago, because He could not possibly have lived as long as this. Heitsi-eibib, the God of the Hottentots in Africa, has died several times, but fortunately has been resurrected just as often. In the Philippines, the grave of the Creator is even now at the cloudy peak of Mount Cabunian.

Haydon suggests that the Eternal One is not much more than three thousand years old, if He is dated from His appearance in human history. Perhaps the concept of immortality was at first beyond man's grasp, because it was not born of the evidence of his senses. He was not ready to pose the deeply baffling question of God's nature and His origin. Apparently, primitive man reasoned along these lines: God created the natural world, and He also belonged to it, He was part of it.

Zeus, though destined to be supreme, is not the Greeks' creator deity. Earth was born of the marriage of Chaos and Eros, a long while before the appearance of the ruling God. Cronus, the father of Zeus, was leader of the quarrelsome Titans. Later, Zeus overthrew him and took his place in Olympus; to his believers, therefore, Zeus was not even beginningless. He seems to have been, at the same time, finite and infinite.

Mostly, the creation myths are very specific, but there are

some exceptions to this rule too. The Chinese mystic, Lao-tzu, had a vision of the unknowable and unnamable Tao in force before heaven and earth. A good phrase for it might be "the primordial principle of existence," a timeless inaction or nonbeing. But paradoxically, since the Tao also moved to create the universe, it was a kind of active being as well. The Tao was and is formless, eternal, unique, insubstantial, and yet it spontaneously sets free the creative powers of the cosmos, and all shapes of life spring from it. The inexhaustible essence of all things, the Tao is omnipresent. So the Tao has brought forth the one, the one has brought forth the two, the two has brought forth the three, and from the three the infinite complexity of the universe has taken shape. In it is the profound dualism of Yang and Yin: the male, active, dry, warm, light phase of cosmic stuff, harmoniously interacting with the female, quiescent, moist, cold, dark phase. Taoism came relatively late—it originated about twenty-five hundred years ago—but since no human concept is *ab ovo*, one supposes that Lao-tzu had intellectual precedents for it. Even so, it predates all other Chinese myths known to us. It is set forth in the *Tao-Te-Ching*:

> *There is a thing inherent and natural*
> *Which existed before heaven and earth,*
> *Motionless and fathomless,*
> *It stands alone and never changes;*
> *It pervades everything and is illimitable.*
> *It may be regarded as the source of the Universe.*
> *I do not know what it is. . . .*
> *I call it Tao and name it as Supreme.*

Such is the meditation of Lao-tzu, who is one of the few authors of creation myths known to us.

Very possibly, too, the translations of Hesiod's *Theogony* perpetuate an error. The Greeks may not have intended to capitalize such words as Chaos and Eros. Their concept may have been like that of Lao-tzu: at the start there was a primal chaos, from which came the earth; and love—the principle of desire—working through it, begot all vital things, such as inhabit the air, the green earth, and the waters. Hesiod, wishing to change his genealogy of the gods into dramatic poetry, could have been boldly personifying abstractions.

Still earlier than the metaphysics of Lao-tzu and Hesiod are those of the Hindu *Rig-Veda*, which date from the twelfth century before the Christian era. They suggest that the gods came later than the cosmos. Even God Himself might not be capable of explaining the formidable question of His origin.

> *Who truly knows, and who can here declare it,*
> *Whence it was born and whence comes this creation?*
> *The Gods are later than this world's beginning.*
> *Who knows then how it first came into being?*

> *He, the very origin of this creation,*
> *Whether he formed it all or did not form it,*
> *Whose gaze controls this world from highest heaven,*
> *He knows it, or perhaps He knows not.*

But by comparison with other Hindu myths, of which there are a host, the hymns of the *Rig-Veda* express an almost modern theology. The earlier myths are far less abstract and give more exact accounts.

The beautiful Zuñi tale (in the Pueblo region of New Mexico) has in it elements of metaphysical abstractness. Awonawilona, the All-Container, is self-conceived. By His own volition, He comes into being, then *thinks* the outward forms of the cosmos, which until now is only void and black desolation. He becomes the sun, mists, clouds, and terra firma of the visible and tangible world. In Colombia, the Uitoto Indians have a tale closely akin. The cosmos is a

dream of their God, Father Naimuena, and His dream is
brought to reality by an unnamed magical substance; at
last, Naimuena leaps on it and stamps it into shape.

The Maoris of New Zealand have a creation chant which
depicts nine successive states of the universal void:

> *Te Kore* (*The Void*)
> *Te Kore-tua-tahi* (*The First Void*)
> *Te Kore-tua-rua* (*The Second Void*)
> *Te Kore-nui* (*The Vast Void*)
> *Te Kore-roa* (*The Far-Extending Void*)
> *Te Kore-para* (*The Sere Void*)
> *Te Kore-whiwhia* (*The Unpossessing Void*)
> *Te Kore-rawea* (*The Delightful Void*)
> *Te Kore-te-tamaua* (*The Void Fast Bound*)

Next come the darkness and light: The Night, the Hang-
ing Night, the Drifting Night, the Moaning Night, the
Daughter of Troubled Sleep, the Dawn, the Abiding Day,
the Bright Day; and, lastly, Whai-tua, which is Space. In
this Space or Ether gather Maku (Moisture) and Mahora-
nui-rangi (Sky), the male and female antecedents of heaven
and earth, not unlike the Yang and Yin of Taoism, and
from them, in time, the Maori gods.

There are, finally, later Hindu and Chinese concepts or
myths which are also predominantly abstract. In India, the
Samhyka philosophers of the eighth century B.C. give the
world this origin: space was condensed out of the void, and
then air out of space. Air gave birth to swirling fire, and fire
to falling water, and water to the element earth. With each
of these five elements was born one of the five senses, to
allow keen perception of it: hearing, touch, sight, taste, and
smell, in turn.

A charming Chinese tale, which is somewhat Platonic in
tone, says that before heaven and earth had become divided, everything was a huge ball of mist; the name of this

circle of mist was chaos. Eventually the spirits of the five elements took form in it, and then developed into five sages. The first was called the Yellow Ancient, and he acted as lord of earth. The second was the Red Ancient, the lord of fire; the third, the Dark Ancient, the lord of water; and the fourth, the Wood Prince, the lord of wood. The last was designated as the Metal Mother, and she became the mistress of metals.

Each of these five venerable sages set in motion the primordial spirit from which he had emanated, so that water and earth sank down; the heavens lifted up and the earth was fixed in its place in the depths. The water welled up into rivers and lakes, and the mountain peaks rose, and valleys between them. The sky cleared and the earth separated; next there were sun, moon, and many stars, sand, heavy clouds, fresh rain, and clinging dew. The Yellow Ancient evoked the pure power of the earth, and fire and water contributed: up sprang the grasses and trees, with their foliage; birds nested in the trees, and the creatures appeared, down to snakes and insects, finny fishes and hard-shelled turtles. Thus gradually came about this world.

But this is about all I can discover in which we are presented with examples of such abstract or semiabstract fantasy. They are largely mental concepts, whereas most of the other creation myths are very different. The ones to follow in this book are common sense; they are more explicable as having been drawn from a beholding of natural phenomena; at best, they are clear metaphors. They have precedent in what can be seen with our own eyes. They are magnifications, however poetic, of facts and processes which mortal man can witness, as the Tao of Lao-tzu is not, and as the self-conceiving of Awonawilona and the vague magical substance of Naimuena are not. Or the nine states of the void of the Maoris, or the emanation of the five ancients from the primordial spirits in the mist . . . we go from this metaphysical poetry to dramatic poetry, far richer in incident and imagery.

II

In the larger body of "beginning" stories, there are five very distinct categories. The first and most widespread of these tells of the world rising from the sea. Even myths of other categories often include this theme of the watery birth.

Very possibly we have here echoes of the deluge myths. The "beginning" stories sound like distorted memories of that hypothetical vast flood which swept over the globe at one time, sparing only a few humans, those in the foothills and mountains. When the waters subsided, the earth seemed to rise again. Men were not witnesses of the first actual creation, so this later upthrust of peaks and plateaus above the oceanic tides might have prompted the Sea Myths. The experience would be awesome, not easily forgotten. It would be described endlessly, and the world might seem to have come into being then. Perhaps aboriginal man had still not developed his memory to the point where it was strong enough to span those waters . . . the abrupt cataclysm divided him from all preceding history, now forever lost. Later, when his imagination sharpened, he peopled that earlier and misty beginning with godlike heroes: only divine figures, larger than human size, had existed then. In every region of the globe, we know, the deluge myths are told, and so aré the creation myths of the earth rising from the ocean; the two watery themes might be closely related, and born of fact.

In the Zuñi epic, to which reference has just been made, the Sun-Father impregnates a foam cap with a ray, and then incubates the cap with his dazzling heat. From the foam, the Beloved Preceder and the Beloved Follower are born. To arm them for heavenly conflict, the Sun-Father gives them a magnificent weapon, a great cloud bow, with thunderbolts to be shot as fatal arrows. The two young gods are also handed fog-making shields, fashioned of clouds and spray. After this preface, the poem continues with a long, involved account of the generation of other gods, and lastly Zuñi man. (And it is, of course, a perfect example of a Solar myth.)

The greatest of India's many stories tells of the primal waters wherein is afloat a golden cosmic egg, from which shall come forth Prajāpati, the creation deity. The egg, or progenitive germ, is formed by the action of *tapas,* the waters' heat, because the desire of the ocean is for divine offspring.

The Egyptian legend recounts how Khepri, the Morning Sun God and Lord of All, first lifts Himself up from Nu, the watery abyss. (Here, too, the Solar motif appears.)

The Sumerian poem explains that the goddess of the primeval ocean gave birth to all the other gods. In the opening verses of the Babylonian story, Apsū, the Abyss and Father of All Beings, is united with Tiāmat, Life of the Womb of the Mountains. Apsū is known as god of freshets and springs, and Tiāmat rules the sea. Their waters are joined into one, and with that the gods come into being. Laḫma and Laḫama are given the gift of light; we identify them as the sun and moon. After them appear Anshar, deity of the sky, and Kishar, deity of the earth.

In Homer, Oceanus is named as the "origin of the gods" and the "origin of all things." He is a river deity and, also in his dual character as a god, an actual river with "inexhaustible powers of begetting." Oceanus is depicted as flowing to the periphery of Earth and then back upon himself in a circle. "Rivers, springs, and fountains—indeed, the whole sea—issue continually from his broad, mighty stream." The circle of Oceanus, as a river, has been fixed by Zeus as the everlasting boundary between this world and the unknown. His mate is Tethys, the conceiving water goddess. Oceanus and Tethys have three thousand sons, rivers all. The daughters, the Oceanids, are of the same large number.

The Spirit of God brooded on the waters, says the *Old Testament*. Some translators take this to mean that, in reality, a stormy wind moved over them. What is implied is that water, wind, and fire existed before the "beginning," in the Hebrew story; and afterward the "wind" was spiritualized into a new and higher concept of Godhead. The Hebrew *Genesis,* it would seem, owes much to Phoenician cosmogony, as found in Philo of Byblus. In the Phoenician account, the wind Kolpias and a woman Baaut procreate the first life. Some linguists interpret Kolpias as referring to "the wind of every quarter," and they note a resemblance between Baaut and *Bohu Tōhū,* an Hebraic term for "primal chaos." The old rabbis picture the creation taking place in darkness and horror, with the rush of a terrible wind.

Such philological demonstrations, however, will seem very strained to some readers. In another instance, Professor William Albright, a Semitic language scholar, has spoken of them as very like an old German student's joke of a philologian who derives the German *Fuchs,* "fox," from the Greek *alopex,* "fox," by lopping off the letters: *alopex: lopex: pex: pix: pux: Fuchs.* Professor Albright also compares this method to that of the slightly addled New England scholar who identified Moses with Middlebury by dropping "—oses" and adding "—iddlebury." My reader must, in the realm of mythology, be prepared for many other "proofs" of this kind.

The Finnish *Kalevala* speaks of a primeval sea into which descends from the sky the virgin daughter of the air, destined to be the Water-Mother. By the action of the tempestuous sea, she finally bears Väinämöinen, who is thus immaculately conceived. But this birth of his takes centuries, during which times she floats without recourse in the elemental cosmic ocean.

In the Far East, the Japanese Shinto myth depicts an original chaos, from which sprang up something that looked like a sprouting reed. This became Kuni-toko-tachi, the One Who Stands Perpetually Over the World, also identified as Ame-no-min-akanashi, the Lord in the Center of Heaven. Yang and Yin, the fertile pair, also came into being simultaneously: in Japanese their names connote High-Producing God and Divine-Producing Goddess. The pantheon was quickly created, thereafter, but much time was to pass before Earth was formed. Then there appeared two later incarnations of Yang and Yin, named now Izanagi, the Impetuous Male, and Izana-ma, the Impetuous Female. They set forth from their Japanese Olympus and followed along the Floating Bridge of Heaven. The god used his spear as a staff, to test the floating trail, and salt water dripping from its jeweled tip clotted below and became the island Ono-Koro, the Self-Congealing, and the very first land. Having started to explore this island in opposite directions, the godly visitors met again on its farther shore and made love there. Their offspring included the sparkling sea, the waterfalls, the soft breeze, the islands of the Japanese archipelago, and the green and fruitful sunlit fields.

Maui, the wily Culture Hero and demigod of the Maoris, is supposed to have pulled up the island of New Zealand from the bottom of the ocean. Mangareva, in the Gambier Group, was also fished up by another Maui, who may perhaps be the same demigod—the deities of the Pacific islands often have similar names but vary slightly in characteristics and powers. The Paumoto Islands were brought up from the watery depths by the god Tekurai, and the more important god Tangaloa lifted up Aneiteum, in the New Hebrides. In archipelagos all over the Pacific, scores of like stories are recited by the savages living there, but for the most part they are legends of how the world—the very small, local one of each island—reappeared after a deluge or engulfing cataclysm, which might have been volcanic in origin. The Iatmul people of New Guinea, in the Sepik region, believe that at one time all land was floating. At a dance pageant given each year, they show how their ancestors pushed these floating lands into their present shape.

The same stories abound in North America. The Bilquala of British Columbia, for example, say that the Earth was raised from the sea by Masmasalanich, who used a strong cable to do it. So that the new-won land would not sink again, Masmasalanich fastened this cable to the sun, to which it is still affixed.

Another northwest Canadian myth relates how the world rose from the waters when Yetl, the Thunderbird, swooped down from heaven. The Creeks and Choctaws, in Oklahoma, have similar tales, but instead of the Thunderbird the act is performed by a pair of doves. Often the labor of piling up the Earth is carried out by an animal helper instead of a god. This form of myth, with its aspects of totemism, is especially common in North America. Amongst such busy world builders, who bring up magic mud from the sea bottom, are the toad, beaver, loon, duck, otter, and muskrat.

When we pass along to South America, we find that some tribes ascribe the world's origin to the water hen. The Caribs of the Antilles give credit to the ibis. In Asia, again, the Shans of Burma say that white ants brought up the solid world from a vast depth.

The Sea myths, thus, have the greatest possible variety. Indians in Brazil trace the beginning to a day when Raini, their deity, placed a large slab of rock on the head of a water god.

The ancient Irish have a tale of Earth rising above the waters; and in one of many versions of the Icelandic *Edda,* Odin, Vili, and Ve slay Ymir, then raise land out of the rimless ocean and give shape to Midgarth.

For many other races, terrestrial life commenced when the sun first escaped from the dark belly of the whale or fish, or the land monster, or the box in which the sun swam in the primeval waves; and along with it appeared all creatures who had sought refuge in the same box or boat to escape the deluge. Once again, here are parallels to the stories of Utnapishtim, Deukalion, and Noah. And again, such tales might seem to bear out the contention of the Solar School of myth interpretation. So might the legend of the Wintu, of Southern California, which dramatically unfolds to the listener how Olelbis, who dwells in a great and handsome "sweat house" in the sky, gathers there the survivors of a fire and flood below, and then repeoples Earth after He Himself weds Mem Loimis, the water.

II

The Sea myths support many other interpretations, of course. The islands of the Pacific were not "fished up" by a god, but they did rise from the blue sea, either as coral aggregations, or as explosive submarine volcanoes, their peaks finally erupting above the boiling waters. Similarly, coastal races of all continents have seen their shores slowly pushed above the hostile, invading ocean. We might suppose the myths to be an allegorical description of that, and hence credit them as essentially historical.

Geography is still another factor in myth interpretation. What is more logical than that people who live on islands or along the seacoast should look upon water as the prevalent element and source of life? Climate and terrain affect the beliefs of mythmakers. Are the tribal storytellers in the tropics or the icelands? Are they hunters or forest dwellers on mountain slopes, or do they fish and sail the seas? Beyond doubt, a people's surroundings and habitual type of work do influence its world view. Glancing back at the myths compiled on the last few pages, we find that, with few exceptions, all belong to races who have quick access to and dependence on the encroaching sea or live beside it.

The Freudians are little impressed by all this, however. They regard any such answer as superficial. They interpret the universality of the Sea myths as a reference to the human foetal condition in water, an identification of human and cosmic birth processes. To them the primal water is to be considered as the womb, the breast of the mother, and the eternal cradle.

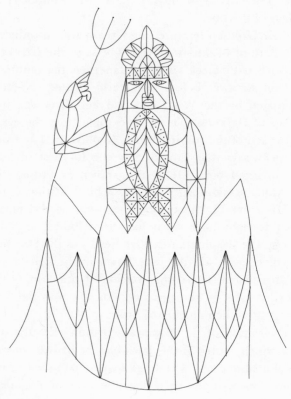

5
THE GOLDEN EGG

A clearer relation to natural birth forms is found in our second category, the World-Egg myths. The most famous of these, the Hindu epic of Lord Prajāpati, has already been mentioned. After the heat of those turbulent waters had created the golden and germinal egg, it floated in the chaotic sea; when finally it was hatched, the androgynous Lord of Creatures came forth from it, to fashion the known universe. Few myths have the simplicity and grandeur of this one.

In their Orphic literature, the Greeks also introduce this theme. Earliest in time was Night—Nyx, to the Greeks. She was a bird with black wings, whom even the omnipotent Zeus held in awe. Before the world existed, Night was impregnated by the Wind and laid her silver egg in the huge lap of Darkness. The first to come from the egg was Eros, the son of the rushing Wind. Kerényi, in *The Gods of the Greeks,* says that Eros is only the loveliest of all the names this god bore. He is also known as Protogonos, a name which acknowledges him to be the "firstborn" of all gods. His name of Phanes describes what he did next: he exposed to light that which had been hidden in Night's silver egg, the sleeping Earth. Overhead was the Sky; below, in the silver oval, was the rest. Then, in the light, the Sky and Earth mated. In another version of this tale, Oceanus and Tethys were in the egg, and this pair was the first to cohabit, under the influence of Eros.

In a variation of the Japanese creation tale, the namelessness which existed at the dawn of time had the beautiful shape of a cosmic egg. The *Chandogya Upanishad* provides an even closer parallel than does the story of Prajápati to the Japanese myth. In this rendering, the two halves of the egg were gold and silver.

After a year's incubation, it split asunder; the golden half became the bright heavens, and the thick white membrane the mountains, the thin membrane of the yolk the mist clouds, and the fluid the sea; all these were in the silver part. Originally this egg developed from nonbeing. There was nothing; then the egg formed.

The Samoans related that Tangaloa-Langi, the Heavenly One, lived in an egg, which he at last broke into pieces, shedding the shell bit by bit. Out of the fragments, the Samoan Islands were formed. Virtually the same legend is told in Tahiti, but here the creator god is called Ta'aroa. He was solitary. He was parentless. He existed lonely in the void. Ta'aroa commanded:

> O landless void, O skyless void,
> O nebulous, purposeless space,
> Eternal and timeless,
> Become the world, extend!

The face of Ta'aroa broke through. The enclosing shell fell away and was the firm land. Earth, shining sea, and sunlit sky had also come into being. Ta'aroa continued to gaze upon his work. He is the source of life, and his curse is death. (This same god, Tangaloa-Langi and Ta'aroa, is also Tangaroa, the popular Polynesian deity.)

On the island of Anaa, there is still another such story. The cosmos was like an egg, in which were Te Tumu and Te Papa. It finally burst and revealed three layers, one above the other; on the lowest level were Te Tumu and Te Papa, who as male and female begot man, creatures, and plants. Matata was the first human being, but he was imperfect and had no arms; he lived only a very short time. The second was Aitu, who was also imperfect, having but one arm and no legs. Third came Hoatea (Sky-Space) who was perfect. After him was created Hoatu (Fruitfulness of Earth), a woman who became his wife. The formation of the world was barely accomplished, when Tangaroa, who sometimes took pleasure in evil, set fire to heaven; but luckily the spread of the flames was observed by Tamatua, Oru, and Ruanuku, who quickly ascended to the sky and extinguished them. Here we see Tangaroa in the role of a creator-destroyer god, not unlike the Hindu Siva; and the myth of the world blaze reappears.

The Finnish *Kalevala,* as we have seen, depicts how for a length of seven centuries the Water-Mother floats with her child Väinämöinen in her swollen womb, unable to give him birth. She raises her hands in prayer to Ukko, who despatches a teal to build its nest on her knee. The teal's eggs roll from the knee and break: the fragments become the earth, sky, sun, moon, and clouds. Now the Water-Mother, drifting still, also like Lord Prajâpati, undertakes the task of world-shaping. She lifts her head from the waves and begins the creation of Order; first she causes it to prevail on the expanse of ocean. Wherever she points her hand, jutting headlands spring up. Wherever she rests her feet, fish caves are formed. When she dives beneath the surface, the depths of the sea are hollowed. When she turns toward the land, the level shores extend. When she touches the shores with her feet, spots for salmon netting are shaped. When her head touches the land lightly, the curving bays are rounded. The Water-Mother floats further out and again abides in the open sea; rocks in mid-ocean are created, and the invisible reefs on which ships are eternally to be shattered, while luckless sailors drown.

After Lao-tzu's time, the Chinese accept P'an Ku as their creator deity. They turn from the Tao, an abstract and metaphysical vision, to a more childish and fanciful myth, perhaps of Indo-Chinese origin. The first half of P'an Ku's name connotes "eggshell," while the second half suggests "firm" or "secure." Some translators, however, hazard that the second half really indicates an "original abyss."

The Persians and Phoenicians also have egg-source myths. Egyptian thought, as disclosed in *The Book of the Dead,* was much concerned with the image of the cosmic egg. It is, to borrow a term, a "mythologem" found widely, though mostly amongst the intellectually higher races.

II

Once again we have a category of "in the beginning" stories which might lend itself to interpretation by the Lunar and Solar Schools. The symbol of the silver or golden egg could have been inspired by man's awed contemplation of the moon or sun. Easily enough, too, the myths might be recognized as a simple development in the history of primitive science. Early man patterned them on what he knew of the life around him.

But the Freudians claim the golden egg stories for their own. The same motif in dreams would have sexual significance, possibly expressive of the child's incest feelings toward his mother. He and his whole world have come from the "cosmic egg," and his one dominant wish is to return to the womb.

6

OUT OF THE MONSTER

A larger and more curious cluster of myths is that which
sees the creation preceded by an act of dismemberment.
In all these, the cosmos is carved out of some slain monster's
body. In a late Rig-Vedic hymn, the Hindus have a classic
example of this. The giant Purusha is killed by the
other gods, and he is sacrificed to form the firmament and
world. His head becomes the sky, his navel the ether, his feet
the earth. Indra and Agni and the Brahmans spring from
his gaping mouth, and his breath is transformed into

Vāyu, the wind, his mouth into the moon, and his eye into Sūryā, the sun; so even the newer gods are born of his parts.

To follow Hindu cosmology is a complex task. We must remember that India, like China, is a continent and has a multiplicity of myths. In the immense passing of time, too, the stories have grown very subtle and intricate: the gods change their names and attributes, and sometimes even their sex. It happens to the Egyptian and Greek deities, as well; and the Babylonian legends also undergo the same sort of baffling metamorphosis. In the mythology of all these races, the almost identical basic motifs have many variations: yet we can always recognize how they are fundamentally alike.

Sūryā, the God of Light, becomes the Hindu creation deity. His steady gaze, as the sun, bestows the gift of life. From him derives Savitr, or Soma, from whom descends Prajāpati, whose tale (of birth from the golden egg in the primal waters) supplants that of the murdered Purusha. But still later a legend in the *Vedas* tells us that the world has been formed by the gods from the quartered parts of Viraj, who has also been sacrificed. So the theme of dismemberment returns persistently.

The *Prose Edda* relates how Ymir, the Rime Giant, came into being in the original void when heat from the south began to melt the streams of ice that ever moved down from the north; a mist arose, and from it fell a drizzle which congealed to hoarfrost. Of the dripping rime, Ymir took shape, supine and inert. The hermaphroditic Ymir slept, and as he did so he perspired: one of his feet begat with the other a son, while beneath his moist left hand a man and woman were created. The mist and frost continued to drip: Adumla, a cow, took form from it. Four jets of milk spurted from her udder, which nourished the sleepy Ymir. For her own nourishment, the magically conceived cow licked the salty ice blocks. In the twilight of the first day, a man's hair came forth from the blocks she licked; the next day the man's head; and the third the whole man, Buri. The son of Buri was named Borr, and Borr married one of the granddaughters of Ymir, who gave him three sons, Othin, Vili, and Ve.

The sons of Borr slayed Ymir, and drowned nearly all the other Rime Giants in his blood. They carried his body to the midst of the Yawning Void. The firmament and earth were constructed from his huge corpse; his skull became heaven, and his brains the storm clouds; his flesh was the land, his bones were the crags; gravel and stones were from his teeth and grinders, and his blood and sweat became the sea. Trees were made from his hair. The *Edda* hails this as wondrous craftsmanship, as it certainly is!

The Indo-Chinese P'an Ku began as a dwarf, girt in a bearskin, or else wrapped in an apron of leaves, to signify his primeval modesty. Two horns sprouted from his head. He grew for eighteen thousand years, increasing his height by six feet daily, changing himself into a giant. Finally he died and achieved a new life. By magic his body was transformed: his brow became the snow-capped mountains, his breath the stormy wind and clouds, his voice the deep thunder, his limbs the four quarters, his flesh the fertile soil, his blood the raging rivers, his beard the bright stars, his skin and hair the thick grasses, bushes and trees, his bones and marrow the ores, rocks, and precious gems; his sweat the sweet rain. Concerning this fanciful myth, Newberry remarks that the cosmos for the Chinese appears to have been a self-created giant whose vital powers are destined to be the source of life, but only after his death and mutilation.

In this category, the Sumero-Babylonian myth is even more significant. Though it lacks the beauty and grandeur of the other stories, it is one that commands our closest attention. Apsū and the Mother Dragon Tiāmat beget the gods, but their quarrelsome children rebel against them. Apsū is overcome and slain, cut to pieces. The furious Tiāmat creates eleven new gods of demonic force to support her against the father killers. (These new eleven are also destined later to provide the names for the signs of the Zodiac.) On the other side, the rebels elect Marduk—also called Bel—as their leader. He is the son of Ea, the water deity, who is the offspring of Anu, the rain god; but the name Marduk also identifies him as the "Male Child of the Sun."

In his chariot, Marduk sets out for battle, with his bow and trident, club and net. Fierce winds convoy him. The horses drawing his chariot are soon flecked with foam. Marduk catches the wildly enraged Tiāmat in his net, and looses a terrible wind in her face. He wounds her with his trident. One of his antagonists flees into the monstrous womb of the dragon-goddess, and Marduk pursues him even there. They fight fiercely there, and the victory is Marduk's. He finally binds his opponent, and attacks the writhing Tiāmat and pierces her heart. The battle won, Marduk climbs upon the dragon's hinder parts and smashes the skull of the Mother Goddess with his club.

The avenger rests, then he cuts the huge body in two. From the severed halves he devises the heavens, and the dry land, and the waters beneath the earth, appointing them the domains of Anu, Enlil, and Ea. He fixes the track of the planets and the circling course of the moon, and sets his godly enemies as the Zodiacal signs in the sky.

According to some Orientalists, the Hebrew *Genesis* originally told of the world having been shaped out of a huge serpent or sea beast, but this has been obscured in ancient translations. These scholars equate the Hebrew *Tōhū* with Tiāmat. Once again we are offered a tenuous philological "proof," which we may hesitate to accept. But the influence of other Sumero-Babylonian myths on Jewish cosmology is often discernible.

This is also true of the elaborate Persian creation myth, which seems to be derived from the Babylonian. Ahura Mazda, the Wise Lord of the Persians, came to them after having undergone changes in the versions of Assyrian and other Semitic storytellers. He is somewhat abstract, for the Persians are subtle, and nowhere more markedly so than in their metaphysics. But the myth, though spiritualized, is still specific, as follows:

Ahura Mazda has water flow from a spring, which is also the goddess Ardvī Sūra Anāhita (the Wet, Firm, Chaste One). The other gods, of the same number as the planets, are also created by Him. Endlessly, too, Ahura Mazda is engaged in combat with Angra Mainyu, the Spirit of Evil and Darkness.

Everywhere in the universe the same eternal struggle is waged by the forces of good and those hostile to them. In particular, Sirius, the god of summer showers, is balked by the demon of drought. Sirius regains the ascendancy by leaping into the sea; the heated waters boil over in tidal waves and steam up to gather as clouds which pour down as rain. (An echo here, of a fire-and-deluge tale?) By the fertilizing action of the waters, thirty-three different lands are produced. (The myth of the watery birth?)

The central region, which is surrounded by six others, is "penetrated" by the dark and evil Angra Mainyu. The ground is shaken, while the mountains arise: in other words, the hostile spirit causes earthquakes and volcanic eruptions. Hera Berezaiti, later to be Paradise, is the loftiest of the new peaks, and here stands and flourishes *haoma,* the plant of life. Ameretat, the genius of plants and giver of immortality, helps to prepare the fields by grinding up seedlings and commingling them with the water gained by Sirius, who sprinkles this beneficent elixir over the barren slopes: the plants sprout like hair on the heads of men.

The most fecund source of growth is the Oxhorn Tree, the "White *Haoma*," which contains in it the germ of every plant, and stands in the midst of the Wide-Gulfed Sea. It holds the power of rebirth for the cosmos, and can grant everlasting life. Sīmurgh, the sacred eagle, frequently alights there. When he spreads his wings and darts off, the tree is so disturbed that a thousand twigs shoot out. When Sīmurgh perches there again, he breaks off the thousand twigs, scattering varied seeds in every direction. The seeds are collected by Camrōsh, another eagle, who carries them to Sirius. In summer showers, the Lord of Rain spreads the seeds everywhere.

The tireless Spirit of Evil, Angra Mainyu, tries to prevent this eternal process of rebirth; he sends a lizard to destroy the "White *Haoma*." To frustrate this, Ahura Mazda creates ten sacred fish which swim about the ocean-rooted tree in a circular formation; the lizard is always faced by one of the wheeling fish. This struggle between good and evil will go on until the world is formed anew.

The production of fire is Ahura Mazda's fourth act, but the priests of the fire-worshipping Zoroastrians have kept His means of doing so a secret out of "pure-mindedness." (Fire, in early myth, often has a sexual origin; hence, the myth is discreetly silent concerning this.) The priests merely state that the creation of flame has come to pass; whereupon the Evil Spirit, jealous, blights its brightness by clouding it with smoke. (Ahura Mazda, like many Culture Heroes who afterward become divinities, is here depicted as a Fire Bringer, too.)

Lastly, the animals are provided. The Wise Lord fashions a sacred ox which, like the Oxhorn Tree, contains the germs of every kind of creature. As the battle goes on, the implacably hostile Angra Mainyu kills the ox, and even Ahura Mazda's antidote cannot restore it to life. But out of the ox's body spring fifty-five varieties of grain and twelve kinds of healing plants and herbs. His testicles yield his semen, which is purified in the moon; from it there come to life a bull and a cow and one hundred and eighty-two other pairs of creatures. We thus see the Persian myth to be an embellished and refined version of a Dismemberment Myth, as well. In some details it is plainly so; but mostly it is only metaphorically so.

Less subtle is the Greek story. The youngest Titan, Cronus, waylays Uranus, his father, emasculates him with a sickle, and hurls the torn flesh into the sea below. The Furies spring from drops of blood which spatter on the earth; from the foam which gathers about the bit of mutilated flesh as it floats on the ocean, Aphrodite arises. Cronus deposes his castrated father and weds Rhea, his own sister. Uranus predicts that Cronus, too, will have his rule usurped by a son; to prevent this, the unfatherly Cronus swallows all his children except the youngest, Zeus, whose existence has been kept secret by Rhea. Zeus finally prevails over his ghastly father, Cronus, and forces him to disgorge his other offspring. Of all Dismemberment Myths, none is more bloody or horrible.

Let us look further around the world. The Kabyles, in Africa, have a tale about the giant Ferraun, to whose parts the cosmos owes its being. The Yoruba, another African group, tell how the goddess Yemaja, pursued by her amorous son, falls backward on the ground just as he is about to seize her. Her black body begins to swell. From each of her breasts a stream of water gushes forth, and her belly bursts open. Out leap fifteen new deities, including those of War, Lightning, and Vegetation.

The dissevered monster of the Gilbert Islanders, out in the Pacific, is a primeval sea serpent.

We have already heard some of the myth of Izana-gi, the Japanese creator deity, from the *Ko-ji-ki*, the *Records of*

Ancient Matters. The story is also told in Korea. In both lands, the myth ends with Izana-gi's death and dismemberment, in this fashion:

In giving birth to the God of Fire, his mother Izana-ma is fearfully burned. She withdraws to the nether world. All vegetation dies, scorched by the dread heat which is now loose in the world. (Again, a fire story.) Izana-gi engages the Fire God in battle and hurls lightning bolts at him. During this combat, a Storm God is born with each stroke of Izana-gi's weapon, seven such deities in all.

When the Fire God is routed and killed, Izana-gi searches for his wife, very much as Orpheus seeks Eurydice; but he is horrified to find her hideously charred and disfigured. She has ordained that he shall meet her in darkness, but he is too impatient and curious (like Orpheus) and has lighted a tooth from the left comb in his headdress as a little torch. What he sees is Izana-ma rotting from her burns, the maggots swarming. The god is aghast; he ungallantly flees, but Izana-ma follows him. Izana-gi delays her by dropping peaches for her to eat—she is quite famished—and makes his escape. (This incident in the tale reminds one of Atalanta, who is similarly tricked by the golden apples of Hippomenes.) The furious goddess, shamed and scorned, vows to exterminate her husband's offspring. Vengefully, she kills a thousand of them each day, but he outpaces her by giving birth to fifteen hundred men and women every twenty-four hours. In doing this, he is polluted by mortality, and it leads to his own end. He bathes in a stream, hoping to cleanse himself, but he dies there to vitalize the world, much as did P'an Ku. Now he is magically transformed. His breath as he is blowing his nose becomes Susa-no-wo, the tempestuous Storm God; his right eye Tsuki-yo-mi, the Moon God, and his left eye Amaterasu, the Sun Goddess, later the ruling Japanese deity. (Still another puzzling Greek resemblance is observed here. One is put in mind of the birth of Pallas Athene from the brow of Zeus. Or of the Indian goddess Tārā, who is miraculously born of a tear which falls from the left eye of her husband, the great Bhodisattva Avalokiteśvara, as he is gazing in pity upon the suffering world.)

The Japanese *Nihongi* relates that Izana-ma herself defies death long enough to give birth to the deities Water, River-Leaves, Gourd, and Clay-Mountain Lady. A later goddess, born of the Clay-Mountain Lady, is the Young Growth Deity, source of the mulberry, the silk worm, and many kinds of grain. A granddaughter is the great Food Goddess, Toyo-Uke-Hime-no-Kami. So, as Newberry points out, the theme of the death and resurrection of a fertility and vegetation deity appears in this story. In fact, that pattern nearly always goes hand in hand with the Dismemberment Myth.

II

Early man seems to have held the idea that the creative act could only follow the killing or suicidal self-sacrifice of the progenitive god. In the myths of Purusha, Viraj, Tiāmat, Ymir, P'an Ku, and Izana-gi, we have the prototype of the death and mutilation of the fertility god, who is later to take a new form and name as the Divine Scapegoat: Tammuz, Osiris, Dionysus, and finally the Christian Saviour, as Frazer suggests. Sometimes the Dismemberment Myth depicts the original creation; sometimes it describes rebirth after the world's destruction. But a violent death as a precondition of life reborn is a theme which runs through nearly all early religions.

Why does daydreaming man see the cosmos in the form of a monster, and why does he insist upon having it torn apart? We may consider several interesting theories about this which have been offered by Rank, Campbell, and others; but for the sake of simplicity I should like to defer discussion of them until we have gone a little further.

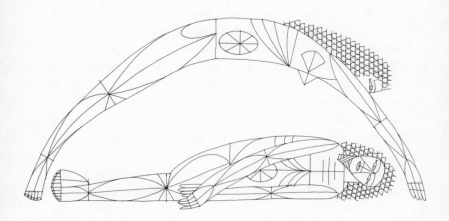

7

THE MATING
OF THE GODS

The mating of the Sky and Earth deities is often a vital
link in the cosmological chain. The twain give birth to
lesser gods, or to the universe, or to forms of life here
below. So frequently is this mating referred to in creation

tales, that it rivals the Sea Myth as the most popular of man's fantasies about the world's origin.

In the Egyptian story, Nut—the Sky—is a goddess, and Seb—the Earth—is a god. This couple, in iconography, are depicted as a female figure arched quite obligingly over a recumbent male.

But usually the Sky is the Father-God. The ancient Chinese and the early Hindus, with their rich and endless store of Vedic hymns and legends, have such a myth. So have the Norse and Germans. The Semites, too.

Since the Sky is the only source of impregnating heat and light, and the Earth outspread supinely beneath it becomes a fecund womb, the analogy is simple, logical. Perhaps one need not read any deeper significance into the recurrence of this theme or motif or assume that it was intended literally. Yet to dismiss it as merely a metaphoric image might be a mistake. In addition to the basic analogy, the stories have other striking likenesses.

The Greeks, in yet another version of the creation, tell how Earth (Gaea, Gaia, or Ge) bore Heaven (Uranus) and then mated with her great son to procreate the Titans, who included Cronus and Rhea. As Kerényi paraphrases Hesiod's account, "Gaia, first of all, and as her equal, gave birth to Uranus, the starry Sky, so that he should completely cover her and be a firm and everlasting abode for the blessed gods."

Gaea's labors were not yet ended. "She bore the great Mountains, whose valleys are favourite dwellings of goddesses, the Nymphs. She bore also that desolate, foaming sea, the Pontos. And all those she bore without Eros, without mating. To Uranus she bore, besides the Titans and Titanesses, also three Cyclopes: Steropes, Brontes, Arges. These have a round eye in the middle of the forehead, and names that mean thunder and lightning." This particular Greek story is a very long and involved one, but it will fascinate all mythologists.

Similar legends of Sky and Earth matings are heard amongst the African tribes and the Indians of North America. An example is the Zuñi *Genesis:* After Awonawilona has brought himself and the outward forms of the universe into being, he creates the Earth-Mother and the All-Covering-Sky. Lying together amorously upon the world-waters, this pair produce the race of man and all other living creatures. Weary at last, the Earth-Mother repulses the Sky-Father, growing big and sinking deep in the embrace of the waters below, separating herself forever from the Sky-Father, who is himself lost in the embrace of the waters above, the mist, clouds, and fresh rain. (Few epics achieve the grandeur of this North American Indian dramatic poem.)

The Luiseño of California relate that at first all is empty space. Ke-vish-a-tak-vish is the sole being. After a long era, and great upheaval—a period of things falling down and working in darkness, then a birth of light—Ke-vish-a-tak-vish creates a male Sky and a female Earth. Like Nut and Seb, the ancestral couplers are brother and sister, yet conceive all living things.

Frobenius has collected Sky and Earth mating myths from all over Oceania in the Pacific. Buck has added to their number. The famous Polynesian "beginning" tale, which possibly is very old and originated in Indonesia, calls the first pair Atea-Rangi, the male Sky, and Papa (or Haka-hotu) the Earth-Mother. Their offspring are the divinities Tané, Rongo, Ru, Tangaroa, and others. We have already met some of these, when examining the Samoan and Tahitian Egg stories.

Needless to say, the Freudians make much of these Sky-Father and Earth-Mother myths, because they contain much obvious sexual symbolism. An incest motif recurs in them inescapably. It is to be found in the Egyptian legend, the Greek legend, and scores of others. Either the divine Mother conjugates with her Son, or the Sister with the Brother. (The incest motif is not confined to Sky-and-Earth myths: Izana-gi and Izana-ma are August Brother and Sister, as are the begetting deities in many other categories of creation tales. Very often, as we shall see later, Twin-ship is involved.) Probably this is partly because the first gods are so few, they and their offspring have little choice but inbreeding; there is no alternative. A rare exception is a variant Egyptian tale of a demiurge creating Earth by an act of masturbation.

But the Freudians stress another motif which is very frequent in primitive myth: the Sky-Father and the Earth-Mother, while embracing, are separated by their children or, particularly, by one son—later to be the Chief God or at least the semidivine Culture Hero—who comes between them and forces them apart. He does this not gently but with brutal strength. A deep anger, even hatred, is given expression.

A vivid instance of this is the Polynesian myth, told in New Zealand, Tahiti, and the Cook Islands. The divine offspring are cramped in darkness and determine to pry apart their parents to obtain light and space. The young god Tané becomes the leader of this rebellious group. He first tries to push the Sky-Father upward by the strength of his arms but fails to do so. In a second effort, Tané stands on his head and exerts more pressure with his feet, and this succeeds. Sky and Earth are permanently divided. Tané is the Tree God, and the Polynesians say that trees emulate his fabulous posture. The roots are the hair of the head, and down in the ground; and the branches are the feet holding up the sky. Only when the Sky-Father is relegated to his present position are the gods able to stand upright in a bright, wide world. And then Tané hangs the sun, moon, and stars on the breast of the Sky-Father, who continues to reign above all.

In some renderings of this tale, the young gods are still in the womb when they plot their rebellion. The Sky lies so close on the belly of the Mother that the divine offspring cannot break free. "Some were crawling . . . some were upright with arms held up . . . some lying on their sides . . . some on their backs, some were stooping, with their heads bent down, some with legs drawn up . . . some kneeling . . . some feeling about in the dark." In the long blackness, they desperately debate whether to slay their parents or forcibly separate them, if possible. Tané says: "It is better to rend them apart, and to let the Heaven stand far above us, and the Earth lie under our feet. Let the Sky become a stranger to us, but the Earth remain close to us as our nursing mother." In this decision there are certainly Oedipal adumbrations, if only in the rejection of the father and the display of preference for the other parent.

The Zuñi story is not much different. Uanam Ehkona, the Beloved Preceder, and Uanam Yáluna, the Beloved Follower, want the earth to become warmer and fitter for life, so with their strong cloud bow they lift the Sky-Father into the high blue vault.

The Egyptian deities, Nut and Seb, are forced apart by their son Shu-Heka, the God of Air. And, in another version of the Sumerian epic, the Sky-Father An and the Earth-Mother Ki are separated by their son Enlil, also the God of Air. The son then unites with his fruitful mother to beget the human race.

The psychoanalysts are even more impressed by the stories which tell not only of a young son's forcing asunder of the First Parents, but also of his savage mutilation and perhaps emasculation of the Primal Father. Cronus ambushes and castrates Uranus, with the help of Gaea—the Earth-Mother—who gives her son the weapon, a sickle with jagged teeth. We have also beheld the Primal Father Apsū and the Primal Giant Ymir slain in open battle or with stealth by their unfilial descendants. The instances of this are legion. The Earth-Mother is depicted as repulsing the Sky-Father, or else the son parts them violently, or the son commits an outrage, very likely of a sexual nature, on the body of the father. Is this dismemberment symbolic of a jealousy of the father? Is the Oedipal tendency so age-old in the reveries of the human race?

In many other myths, the hero is self-created, which the Freudians say is a disguise to deny a debt to the father. But such daydreams, as Otto Rank suggests, might rather be expressive of man's self-creative instinct, which makes him reluctant to grant credit for his own development and accomplishment to either parent. That may also account, Rank says, for the so-called "swallowing myths," those in which the son or Culture Hero—whether he be the Eskimos' Raven or the Blackfeet's Kut-o-yis or the Finns' Väinämöinen or the Greeks' Heracles or Perseus or the Babylonians' Marduk or the Hebrews' Jonah—cuts or forces his way out of the womb or bowels of a monster: the Primal Mother, or Tiāmat, or else a nameless dragon or whale or fish. Whenever this deed is described, the mythmakers deem it an heroic act. To the Freudians, it is a pure example of birth symbolism.

Joseph Campbell, in *The Hero with a Thousand Faces,* puts forward a different interpretation of the slaying and rending apart of the monster. "The myths never tire of illustrating the point that conflict in the created world is not what it seems. Tiamat, though slain and dismembered, was not thereby undone. Had the battle been viewed from another angle, the chaos-monster would have been seen to shatter of her own accord, and her fragments move to their respective stations. Marduk and his whole generation of divinities were but particles of her substance."

To some, Campbell's reading of the myth will seem far too subtle an intention for the mind of early man. They will feel much the same about Rank's analysis of it. The orthodox Freudians appear to offer a more plausible explanation, but it is still very hypothetical.

8
THE EDICT

The fifth and final category of creation stories is that which describes the world as brought into being by the utterance of a demiurge. These are the Edict myths; they derive from primitive man's deep respect for the magic of the spoken word.

Khepri, the morning sun, the first deity in the Egyptian

pantheon, creates himself by uttering his own name. In another Egyptian myth, Thoth calls the gods into existence by his powerful words.

Lord Prajāpati, after he arises from the golden cosmic egg, utters the sacred exclamations *Bhus, Bhuvah, Svar* and thereby conjures up earth, atmosphere, and sky. Every mythical theme, indeed, is combined in the Hindu legends. The watery birth, the cosmic egg, the dismemberment, the mating of the gods, and the creative edict. The same, in equal measure, is true of the Egyptian and Greek stories, and the Finnish epic.

In the Mayan *Popul Vuh,* the Quiché report how the gods sit in a shining circle of light. Nothing else has being, except a vast quiet sea and a sunless sky. In this silence, the gods are lonely.

They yearn for attention from someone. After a colloquy, they command: "Earth!" and instantly land springs up in the white-capped ocean. The gods then command the existence of jungle-sloped mountains, green trees, and animals, all by mere words.

The Uitoto creation myth (told in Colombia) also starts off by relating, "In the beginning the word gave origin to the Father."

The lore of the North American Maidu Indians says that at first there was only water and the Coyote cried, "Let the surf become sand!" and it did. The god Nichant, of the Gros Ventre Indians of Montana, fashioned a circle of mud just wide enough for him to stand on. Stepping on this, Nichant closed his eyes and demanded: "Let there be land as far as my eyes can see!" When he opened his eyes once more, the surrounding water had gone; the land was there.

In the Tahitian story, which has already been mentioned, Ta'aroa gives the world extension by his bare pronouncement.

The Sumerian *Gilgamesh* explains that Heaven and Earth were separated because the name of man had been ordained and the surface of the Earth was to be his dwelling place. The "naming" of things, designating a word to them, is the creative magical act.

The Hebrew *Genesis,* which owes so much to the Sumero-Babylonian, is the best known of all edict stories, of course. "And God said, 'Let there be light,' and there was light. And God said, 'Let there be a firmament in the midst of the waters, and let it divide the waters from the waters.' " We can only suppose, from what we know of ancient Jewish thought, that the authors of *Genesis* were wholly literal about the creative force of God's edict.

By way of the Greek concept of Pneuma-Logos, belief in the magic power of the word later enters into Christianity. John proclaims: "In the Beginning was the Word. All things were made by the Logos; without Him nothing was made that was made." Or others declare: "And the Word was made flesh." The Incarnate Word.

In medieval times, the Jewish Cabalists, who either borrowed from Chinese thought or had an inherent affinity with it, were certain that God had created the world by ten utterances of *sphirot.* That mystic belief was current throughout all the Orient. The different parts of the world, according to the Cabalists, had demiurgic counterparts in the twenty-two letters of the Hebrew alphabet. The clue is disclosed in the *Sefer Yzira, The Book of Creation,* an esoteric Jewish work that first appeared in Babylonia some two thousand years ago.

Supposedly God Himself had composed it, with Abraham's help. The Talmudists learned exactly by what letters or combination of letters God had brought the world into existence. The four letters of His Ineffable Name, the Tetragrammaton, in particular, had an occult significance and power; therefore, the pious and scholarly elite who knew the names of the angels could also control the forces of nature. They pored long and hard over their books to master them. Even a century ago, in the writings of Ballanche, the illuminist, we read: "God spoke and the chaos took on shape. God spoke only once, but for God once means always, and the world existed for all time."

This faith in the potent word, still lingering in corners of our civilization today, can be traced earlier than the Cabalists and Talmudists to the Babylonian Geonim; and before them to the Zoroastrians, whose Ahura Mazda lists words in the order of their holiness. Ahura Mazda, the Wise Lord, also lists His own many sacred names; some, when spoken aloud by the purely devout, have more fiend-smiting strength or healing effect than others.

In *Art and Artist,* Rank suggests that the craft of poetry descends from this belief in the creative potency of the word, as it was first expressed in incantatory prayers. The priest, the tribal poet, could control or obtain things by solemnly naming them; and he could bring back forgotten past events, even the dead, by evoking them in words.

II

Also in *Art and Artist,* Rank considers the Dismemberment and Edict myths and submits a new interpretation of them. The mythical primal giants reflect a cosmic extension of early man into the universe. This is like Schopenhauer's idea of the *"makanthropos."* The world has been formed out of Ymir and Purusha and Viraj and P'an Ku and the other vanquished monsters, because actually man has fashioned his concept of the world in his own physical image. Man begins by naming the parts of his own body, and then names the parts of the universe by human metaphors, especially in his astrology and astronomy. When the giant is dismembered, his head is always the heavens, his bones the mountains, his veins the rivers. So it all fits very nicely.

Along with this, Rank contends that the "seat of life" or the "soul" was first believed by early man to be in the lower part of his body, and that the "place of the soul" has slowly risen in the human frame to the head. Rank cites a great deal of evidence whereby this rise and change in concept can be traced in man's earliest culture: in his architecture, pottery and painting, poetic myth.

For example, states Rank, the "seat of life" was once supposed to be in the uterus, or in the nearby liver and entrails, or near the navel. Consequently, man's earliest dwelling is the protective cave, whose shape is uterine. (The Freudians assert that it was an impulse to return to the womb that first led man to seek shelter in caves. His first deliberate architecture is the tomb, also a dark enclosure. It represents to Rank, however, not so much the mother's body as the recesses of one's own, that part of the body where the soul supposedly resides.) Later, as in Crete, man prefers to build everything in the form of the labyrinth, which resembles the entrails. In that cultural era, even the décor of his palaces shows the same intricacy of line. Similar labyrinthine spirals are found in Nordic regions; and a very like design, based on the pattern of the entrails, is commonly seen on grave steles and reliefs in Egypt and Babylonia, as well as on the better known ones in Crete.

In Babylonia, the words for "soul" and "liver" are synonymous. The liver mantics, foretelling the future by reading entrails and the liver, practiced their magic art there. Many Greeks and Romans also considered the liver rather than the brain to be the seat of thinking power and desire and instincts.

One may question whether aboriginal man sought shelter

in a cave for any other reason than to get out of the rain, but a study of the illustrations accompanying Rank's text and the historical instances provided by him does strengthen his strange contention. He makes out a scholarly case for it, at least.

Next, the navel. It becomes all-important a few centuries later, says Rank. Greek temples are built around the navel stone, or omphalos. In every part of Greece thrive mystic cults hoping to worship at the "earth navel," the fissure at the very center which leads to the underworld. According to one belief, this fissure was at Delphi. But perhaps it was elsewhere.

The new cult of the omphalos enters into all ancient house and city planning which revolves about a marked center, the circular *mundus*. Even ritual ploughing follows this circular design. The largest and most sacred building is always at the center of the town, and so is the most important and sacred city deemed to be the earth-navel, from which milestones measure the distance, whether from Athens, Jerusalem, or Rome. (Joseph Campbell, in *The Hero with a Thousand Faces*, also examines this theme of the World Navel and lists many instances of it in myth, from the Volga to the Ganges. The center of the world may be in Siberia where the White Youth of the Yakuts is born, or under the Bo Tree where the Buddha sits, or at the spot where Kali stands; or in the circle drawn by the Pawnee Indians of Nebraska; or it may be on the Isles of the Blessed, or in the Persians' Paradise, or at the place where Wotan died or Attis was crucified on a tree, or at Calvary where Jesus hung on the Holy Rood; or in Mecca with its black stone.)

Whenever the "place of the soul" rises in the body, the shape of pottery and other artifacts reflects it. This leads Rank to a very interesting discussion of the evolving Greek architectural column as an imitation and abstraction of the human body, as is best evidenced to him by the forms of the caryatids, the sculptured female figures that support entablatures. But finally primitive man develops language, the throat and mouth are of prime importance, words are magical, and man's soul is in his breath. Soon after, with the vital center now in the head, his myth and religion are spiritualized, bodiless. His view of the cosmos is, too. He has attained to the Edict Myth, which is the ultimate. By this time, the Babylonians are reading the future not in the liver but in the stars.

9

MYTH AND
THE ARCHETYPE

Earlier we described the premises of a number of schools
of myth interpretation, but not that of C. G. Jung.

In the Freudian heaven, Jung is the Lucifer who several
decades ago led a revolt against the Master. Of all the

dissident Freudians, Jung has been the most interested in mythology and influenced contemporary research into it. He finds in it, indeed, depths that Freud himself never perceived.

Says Jung, sweepingly: "The innumerable attempts that have been made in the sphere of mythology to interpret gods and heroes in a solar, lunar, astral or purely mythological sense contribute nothing of importance to the understanding of them; on the contrary, they all put us on a false track."

Jung acknowledges a debt to Nietzsche, who in *Human all too Human* wrote: "In our sleep and dreams we pass through the whole thought of earlier humanity. I mean, in the same way that man reasons in his dreams, he reasoned when in the waking state many thousands of years ago. . . . The dream carries us back into earlier states of human culture, and affords us a means of understanding it better."

Like many other of Nietzsche's insights, this one is stimulating, but is it true? Jung points to a host of dream analyses which he and his fellow workers have made to affirm it. He goes further. He claims that we could hardly revert so often or deeply to the remote past in our dreams, unless there existed in our minds certain "primordial images" or "archetypes" that are common to all mankind. According to Jungian psychology, there is a striking repetition in our dreams of what might be called "mythical" symbols which defy any ordinary explanation. In many instances, we have no background of conscious knowledge to account for the presence of such symbols in our minds. Even an indirect inkling or derivation of them has to be ruled out. The symbols are not personal, drawn from our individual life experience, but might better be described as racial or universal.

Especially in the dreams of early childhood, Jung goes on, remarkable archetypal contents are brought to light. The same inescapable images are found in the fantasies of psychotics, and in myths, and in the delicate fairy tales to which many once robust myths have finally descended. The Jungians make this distinction: Dreams are formless and often irrational; psychotic fantasies are disordered to the verge of delirium, though like our dreams they do not lack a hidden coherence, which the psychiatrist may uncover. The myth, however, is ordered and largely comprehensible, and the primordial images show themselves most sharply there.

Jung deduces from this: " 'Myth-forming' structural elements must be present in the unconscious psyche." The primordial images are not myths themselves, but the components of myths.

Whereas the dream is largely personal, the myth is an impersonal projection; it arises out of a "collective psychology," or better what Jung calls the "collective unconscious," the unconscious or instinctual life of the whole race of man. This is a bold theory, and one much disputed by some other psychologists who say that no such thing as a "collective unconscious" exists in us; but Jung has won many devoted converts, too. They agree with him that we never outgrow the primitive who lives on within us. We and our ancestors are identical in many ways.

On several occasions, Jung has written vivid descriptions of what he conceives the savage's mentality to be. He says that the savage's conscious mind is far less developed in extent and intensity than our own. Functions such as willing and thinking are not yet divided in him; they are preconscious, which means that he does not think *consciously,* but that thoughts *appear* for him. The savage cannot claim that he thinks; rather, "something thinks in him."

The spontaneity of the act of thinking does not lie, causally, in his awareness, but is still in his unconscious. Moreover, he is incapable of any conscious act of will; he must put himself beforehand into the "mood for willing," or let himself be put in it by the shaman's hypnotic suggestion, for which may be used rites *d'entrée et de sortie,* with singing, stamping, shouting. His conscious mind is menaced by an almighty unconscious; hence his fear of hostile magical influences which may overwhelm him at any moment. "Owing to the chronic twilight state of his consciousness," Jung remarks, "it is often next to impossible to find out whether he merely dreamed something or whether he really experienced it. The spontaneous manifestation of the unconscious and its archetypes intrudes everywhere in his conscious mind, and the mythical world of his ancestors is a reality equal if not superior to the material world. It is not the world as we know it that speaks out of his unconscious, but the unknown world of the psyche, of which we know that it mirrors our outside world only in part, and that, for the other part, it moulds this outside world in accordance with its own psychic assumptions."

In us, by contrast, the archetypes occur involuntarily by means of unconscious processes whose exact nature can only be inferred. The more sophisticated we are, the more we attempt to explain our fleeting glimpse of these primordial images in a rational fashion; but this, Jung declares, is futile. They belong to what is irrational in us. The motifs or primordial images, which are elusive to us, are far sharper to the inner vision of savage man, who also meets them in his myths, where they are embedded in tribal history that goes back countless generations, and where they have long since acquired a traditional meaning which has a profound social and psychological influence on him. He lives under their aegis. Jung, too, assumes that the thought processes of modern savages bear a close kinship to those of prehistoric man. In the myth, therefore, we meet an externalization of early man's preconscious life; and of the life of our own unconscious, too, regardless of how civilized we now like to deem ourselves.

Exactly what does Jung intend by "archetypes" or "primordial images"? He tells us more about how they affect us than what they are, leaving most of that for future discovery by a scientific correlation of dream analysis and myth analysis. Some of his followers, including Kerényi and Campbell, have begun an exhaustive study of the recurrent motifs in world myth as we have already seen: for instance, the adventures of the Culture Hero tend to follow the same pattern everywhere. We have also learned that the world is imagined as having come into being in a few set ways . . . from a watery birth, from a golden egg, from a dead and hacked monster; by the proper or incestuous mating of the gods, by a demiurge's edict. Some of this might be based on a kind of primitive logic and deduction, by early man's observing his environment, but can all of it? Says Jung: "The archetype does not proceed from physical facts; it describes how the psyche experiences the physical fact, and in so doing the psyche often behaves so autocratically that it denies tangible reality or makes statements that fly in the face of it." We do know that this happens in dreams and myth, for instance, when the Culture Hero undergoes his many metamorphoses, or slays the dragon or giant with a god's aid, or is magically transported or gifted; or is swallowed by the open-mouthed and toothless whale, only to escape unharmed. When dreams were linked to myths by Freud, it was because he saw that both have this characteristic of unreality. Jung implies that this propensity to unreality invades our conscious thinking, too, to dominate far more of it than we realize.

A great deal, though not really all, of the Freudian interpretation of myth symbols is ruled out. "These fantasy images are not the 'wish-fulfilments' of the repressed libido," Jung asserts. "These images were as such never conscious and consequently could never have been repressed. I understand the unconscious rather as an *impersonal* psyche common to all men, even though it expresses itself through a personal consciousness. When anyone breathes, his breathing is not a phenomenon to be interpreted personally. The mythological images belong to the structure of the unconscious and are an impersonal possession; in fact, the great majority of men are far more *possessed by* them than possessing them."

There is a reference to the "structure of the unconscious" which suggests that it is a physical structure. Jung apparently makes little or no distinction between body and mind, but holds with Spinoza that they are one. Consequently, he attaches a metaphysical importance to the primordial image; it is our fundamental way of perceiving the world. "The symbols of the self arise in the depths of the body and they express its materiality. The symbol is thus a living body, *corpus et anima.* . . . The deeper 'layers' of the psyche lose their individual uniqueness as they retreat farther and farther into darkness. 'Lower down,' that is to say as they approach the autonomous functional systems, they become increasingly collective until they are universalized and extinguished in the body's materiality, in the chemical bodies. The body's carbon is simply carbon. Hence 'at bottom' the psyche is simply 'world.' In this sense, I hold Kerényi to be absolutely right when he says that in the symbol the *world itself* is speaking. The more archaic and 'deeper,' that is the more *physiological* the symbol is, the more collective and universal, the more 'material' it is." That is why, for Jung and his followers, the archetypal symbols in myth have a rather mystical significance. Ultimately, they are as inexplicable and impersonal as our breathing, or the fact of our being.

What do the archetypes signify? We can never really know. They have their full meaning only in the unconscious, and when we confront them in the light of consciousness where they intrude, they baffle and elude us. To Jung, rational explanations of myths are wholly vain. By the time the symbol has been intellectualized and placed in an allegory where it is directly comprehensible, it has sloughed off much of its true universal character; thus reduced, it is obscure, fragmentary. The more sophisticated we become, the more we are inclined to look upon these mythical symbols with disdain; in our conscious thinking, we pay scant heed to them, and Jung believes that there is a great psychological danger in this.

Probably this much of Jung's theory is as plausible as any other, though of course by its own terms it is not very demonstrable. Some of his followers, moreover, are not always so careful in their "proofs" as they ought to be, for they tend to choose those myths that help to substantiate their claim, while overlooking many which do not; and their analyses of dreams might also be described as arbitrary; not more so than the old-fashioned Freudian interpretation, perhaps, but really not less so.

II

Another phase of Jung's theory is even more controversial. As is well known, Jung's bent is religious; we have already noted his markedly mystical side. He argues, indeed, that the major religious symbols are amongst the primordial images and hence religion is a vital necessity to any mature person. Man suffers by depriving himself of myth or detaching himself from it; his personality lacks integration without participation in it.

Jung attributes to sexual maladjustment only a share, and sometimes a minor one, in the origin of neuroses. Instead, he thinks that man's drift away from the acceptance of myth—from religion—is much more responsible for his present mental ills.

The Jungians refer back to the "perils of the soul" known to us from the psychology of savages. Archetypes are psychic forces that demand to be taken seriously and have a strange way of making sure of their effect. Always they have been the bringers of protection and salvation. Violation of them has its dread consequences.

"The primitive mentality does not *invent* myths, it *experiences* them. . . . Not only do they represent, they *are* the mental life of the primitive tribe, which immediately falls to pieces and decays when it loses its mythological heritage, like a man who has lost his soul. A tribe's mythology is its living religion, whose loss is always and everywhere, even among the civilized, a moral catastrophe. But religion is a vital link with psychic processes independent and beyond consciousness, in the dark hinterland of the psyche."

Man's religions, if they have dreamlike and mythical components, will bear in them these inevitable motifs which are omnipresent in our reveries.

The symbols can be only partly described and interpreted, for they have an unconscious core of meaning. But every interpretation which more or less approximates the hidden sense of these symbols has always, from the very beginning, laid claim in our feelings not only to absolute truth and validity, but to instant reverence and religious devotion. By our very psychological nature and nervous constitution, we are compelled to believe in them. (At the same time, Jung admits that from a skeptical point of view, the *hidden sense* of these symbols might very possibly be deemed only *nonsense*.)

Explains Jung: "What an archetypal content is always expressing is first and foremost a *figure of speech*. If it speaks of the sun and identifies it with the lion, the king, the hoard of gold guarded by the dragon, or the force that makes for the life and health of man, it is neither one thing nor the other, but the unknown third thing that finds more or less adequate expression in similes, yet—to the perpetual vexation of the intellect—remains unknown and not to be fitted into a formula. For this reason the scientific intellect is always inclined to put on airs of enlightenment in the hope of banishing the spectre for once and all. . . . In reality we can never cut loose from our archetypal foundations unless we are prepared to pay the price of a neurosis, any more than we can rid ourselves of our body and its organs without committing suicide. If we cannot deny the archetypes or otherwise neutralize them, we are confronted, at every stage in the differentiation of consciousness to which civilization attains, with the task of finding a new *interpretation* appropriate to this stage, in order to connect the life of the past that still exists in us with the life of the present, which threatens to slip away from it. If this link-up does not take place, a kind of rootless consciousness comes into being no longer orientated to the past, a consciousness which succumbs hopelessly to all manner of suggestions and, practically speaking, is susceptible to psychic epidemics."

Jung thus insists that we must put our faith in something which is forever indefinable: a host of symbols revealed to us in our sacred myths whose real nucleus of meaning is mysterious and irreducible, though always inviting new readings. Failing to yield to faith in them, we imperil our happiness. We should not seek to lead fully conscious lives. We need to reacquaint ourselves with myth; in myth are the omnipotent primordial images, forever beckoning to us.

To some this will sound remarkably like the thinking of D. H. Lawrence. Something like it is also found in the thought of Samuel Butler.

It is an ambitious claim on behalf of myth. This part of Jung's theory, that such archetypes—if neglected or denied— cause neuroses or psychoses, is not our present concern. I have described it here partly because it is such a well-known phase of Jung's psychology that I can hardly omit it. Nor do I take issue with it; simply, it lies outside the scope of my essay, and perhaps much beyond my competence to judge.

III

Why should a Polynesian have a legend which is almost exactly like one told by a Nordic nomad, or a Brazilian Indian repeat a tale much like that of an Eskimo? Jung's theory of the archetype could be one explanation of the universality of myth, the puzzling similarity of the heroic and sacred stories, the dramatic events unfolded in them, amongst all races and in so many far-flung regions of the world.

We have already had Frazer's opinion on this subject. It is partly due, he says, to the fact that the thought processes of human beings are everywhere the same, so that people respond in a like manner to similar "causes." This leads us to ask about the "causes." What were they? Though Frazer does not say so, they could be, quite easily, objective or subjective. If the former, they might have been historical events—actual catastrophes—or have had natural explana- tions—lunar, solar, meteorological. If the latter, they could have had a Freudian or Jungian origin. So Frazer and Jung are not wholly in contradiction.

The esteemed anthropologist, Franz Boas, remarks in *The Mind of Primitive Man:* "Since Waitz's thorough discussion of the unity of the human species, there can be no doubt that in the main the mental characteristics of man are the same all over the world." Boas also cites Adolf Bastian, who in his *Elementary Ideas* complains of the "appalling monotony of the fundamental ideas of mankind all over the globe," and who asserts that certain patterns of associated ideas may be recognized in every culture. Bastian suggests that the "elementary ideas" referred to in the title of his study may be "the spiritual (or psychic) germinal dispositions out of which the whole social structure has been developed organically." This is not a new view, either, as Campbell illustrates; it goes back to classic sources, including the Greek Stoics and their *Logoi spermatikoi.*

Some sort of concept like the archetype seems to be valid and even imperative, with or without the mystical overtones on which Jung insists. If there is not a "collective unconscious," there is at least an inescapable "collective psychology." We do not think as we wish, but as we must.

IV

Although the world's myths have many repetitive motifs, do they not have an even larger number of variations? The answer is yes.

C. Kerényi, the Hungarian mythologist, offers this quick summary in *The Gods of the Greeks:* "Every mythological theme has in every period been the subject of a number of different stories, each of them variously conditioned by the place, time, and artistic powers of the narrator. . . . The *words* of the basic story have disappeared, and all that we have are the variations. But behind the variations can be recognized something that is common to them all: a story that was told in many fashions, yet remained the same."

Something was said before of the geographical factor in accounting for diversity in myths. Kerényi puts aside any discussion of this. "We leave undecided in principle the question of whether the place of origin was an 'ideal' place, that is to say, the possible result of the *human mind's* seeing the same aspect of the 'cosmic content' everywhere in the same image, or whether it was a definitive geographical focus of culture where the great mythological archetypes were created for all time." (I presume that "ideal" is used here in the Platonic sense, of perfect and eternal concepts that are not objective to the senses but are real to thought: the *eida*.)

Kerényi has made a special study of a few of these archetypes, that of the Divine Child, for instance, whom he declares is the forerunner of the Culture Hero and the World Savior. In myth, this child is usually associated with water and is depicted riding on a dolphin's back. His image is found everywhere in early Greek and Oriental art.

Apollo, Kerényi says, had an affinity for the sea, not simply because his birthplace, Delos, was originally a floating island, but because the dolphin was sacred to him. The Greeks call this beast the "uterine creature"—its name means uterus—and Apollo is often known as Apollo Delphinios, because of their relationship. To this, one should add that Apollo once performed the "mighty feat" of slaying a primeval monster, which makes him again typical of the Hero.

In the Hindu legend *Matsya-Purana* (titled after the "fish," *matsya*), Manu, the first man, is quoted by Kerényi as speaking thus to the fish-bodied Vishnu: "How did this world, shaped like a lotus, spring from your navel in the lotus epoch when you lay in the world-ocean? You lay sleeping in the world-ocean with your lotus-navel; how did the gods and the host of seers arise in your lotus in those distant times, called forth by your power?" Vishnu is here a new instance of the Divine Child. He is accordingly (for Kerényi) a symbol of fish, embryo, and womb at once; for the boundless water, like the womb of the mother, is an organic part of the image of the Primordial Child; and the sea beast or fish, too, is a symbol of fertility.

Kerényi notes a particularly clear instance in the provenance of this symbolism: in the so-called theological discussion at the court of the Sassanidae, where reference is made to the mother pregnant with the child god, of Hera-Pege-Myria, which she carries in her womb, as in a sea. Of this mother and child, it is said: "She has but one fish." The Christian allegory of the fish is declared by Kerényi to be a secondary phenomenon in the history of this mythological symbol. Quite clearly he implies that the Christ figure is the ultimate product of these many images of the Divine Child, the dolphin rider; and Jung, in the same book, then analyzes this repetitive image and finds the Child to be hermaphroditic.

Another of the images traced by Kerényi is that of the Kore, the reluctant Mother-Goddess who conceives the Divine Child, perhaps immaculately. Or else she is raped by God or a god. I believe these brief examples will indicate the Jungian approach to myth, which is undeniably circuitous at times; and, since it declares the core of the symbol to be indefinable, can never be quite as specific as some hardheaded thinkers might wish it to be.

We should note that Kerényi is one of the few who speak of the myths as having been conditioned by "the artistic powers of the narrator." Some people would say that we cannot rule out the possibility that the personality of the artist-mythmaker, his individual psychological needs and background, influenced the special turn given to the myths he created or retold, and colored the values he incorporated and sanctioned in them. In their view, it is likely that the one who asked the metaphysical questions, about the origin of the cosmos and man, and the nature of God, was also the one who ventured the quasi-religious answers: he was the aboriginal philosopher, artist, and priest in one.

Jung believes, however, that the individual psychology of the artist has never been of much consequence: the poet is born with an "archaic constitution," and what speaks through him is not his own voice but the "collective unconscious" of the race. He is merely an unknowing instrument of it. (We shall return to a consideration of this later.)

Kerényi does make some allowance for the myth as a work of art, apart from its other facets, but again a mystical strain enters. "The degree of directness of the images presented in dreams and mythology is, to say the least, very much the same. In this respect, dreams and mythology are nearer to one another than dreams and poetry. . . . One must not, of course, altogether disregard the fact that mythology is also fundamentally a special, creative, and therefore also an artistic activity of the psyche. . . . It encroaches on poetry, but nevertheless it is an activity of its own kind, to be ranked with poetry, music, the plastic arts, philosophy and the sciences. Nor should it be confused with spiritual knowledge or theology; from these it is distinguished by its artistically creative character." Mythology is not a branch of any other art, but an art all its own. And Kerényi concludes with a pronouncement resembling Jung's: "The stuff of mythology is composed of something that is greater than the storyteller and than all human beings." As we saw above, in a quotation from Jung about the physical structure of the archetype, Kerényi strongly holds that through the primordial image the *world itself* enters man's unconscious and is revealed to him.

It is a far flight, then, from Malinowski's view of myth to Kerényi's.

10

MAN AND TOTEM

From stories about how the world began, let us now turn to a somewhat different yet inevitably related subject, tales about the first appearance here of man. Most of these stories lack the grandeur of the cosmic myths, but many have charm and even humor. And there is much beautiful poetry in them, too. As I collected them, I found them quite fascinating, because of their odd and whimsical details.

Such tales about the beginning of man fit into four or five large categories which provide even clearer evidence that the human mind seems to work the same everywhere. As always, there are a few exceptions to this rule. The others have the challenging similarity of the Fire-and-deluge myths, the Culture Hero myths, the Divine Child myths, the Creation-of-the-World myths.

For the most part, the stories assume that man existed before a deluge or world-fire, and describe how the land was repeopled after the cataclysm. When the survivor is a lone man, isolated and desperate, he finally mates with a wooden fetish. Or, if only a few men survive, homosexuality is necessary. From these unions, children are born. An element of magic is present!

In a more popular group of legends, a pregnant woman is left solitary following the vast destruction. The story-teller's problem is simpler here. Either the sole woman has twins, a boy and a girl, who grow up and have an incestuous relationship, or she herself sleeps with her son. I could quote a hundred examples of this sort of tale. The Mandayas of the Philippine Islands claim to be descended from a surviving girl, whose husband is dead. She prays for his posthumous child to be a son. The child is. He grows to manhood, and she marries him. The Toradjas of the central Celebes have virtually the same story. In other versions, also popular, the solitary woman is too old to bear children. Her dilemma calls for miraculous help of some kind. She is impregnated supernaturally by the spirit of fire, wind, or rain. Her son is destined to become the tribe's Culture Hero. Here again the theme of his immaculate conception makes its appearance. Sometimes, in these many myths, a demon fathers him.

A more remarkable class of stories, however, brings in an animal helper. To illustrate: The Cashinaua of western Brazil say that when the heavens overflowed, the deluge drowned all signs of life below. In heaven, however, was a woman who was pregnant. Lightning killed her and hurled her down upon the earth. There she was found by a crab, who recognized her condition and cut open her body with its sharp claws and freed her twins, a boy and a girl. The kind crab's wife raised them. In time, the brother and sister wed and became the ancestors of the Cashinaua tribe.

A tale very like this is repeated by the Crees, in Manitoba, many thousand miles to the north. After a flood, only the virgin Kwaptahw is left alive. A bird, clasping her in its claws, bears her over the waters to the top of a high cliff, where she is delivered of twins, a son and a daughter. These are the progenitors of the Crees. (An echo of the Greek fable of Leda and the Swan is heard here, but how can we account for the Greeks and the Crees sharing a story, or even a theme?)

Such stories about an animal helper comprise the first large category of creation-of-man myths. Here is a famous and haunting one which belongs to the Seneca Indians:

> *A woman dwelt in the sky, in the midst of the Blue. She began to have a dream, in which a man appeared and warned her. In her village was a tree with white blossoms; when the blossoms opened the sky was bright, and when they closed the sky was dark. In her dream, the woman was told by the man that the flowering tree should be pulled up. She took this word to the old men of the village, but they paid her no heed until the dream had come to her three times. The villagers were finally impressed and held a council. They dug around the roots of the tree, hop-*

ing that more light would indeed flow in, but instead the tree fell through and disappeared.

In the long darkness that followed, the villagers grew more and more unhappy and angry, and to punish the woman they pushed her through the deep hole in the sky left by the vanished tree. She fell a very long way and finally came out into the bright sky which belongs to us.

Below her was only the vast sea, a waste of waters, populated by creatures that swim. A member of the duck family saw the strange being who was falling toward them. "Look!" cried the duck to the others.

The swimming creatures recognized that the woman could not live in water, as they did, and they quickly got together to discuss how to help her. A fish hawk instantly flew up and caught her and held her, while far beneath a hell-diver plunged to the bottom of the ocean, where no living thing had ever been before, and at last, after several tries, brought up a little mud. This he put on a tortoise's back. While the fish hawk went on holding the woman in the air, the hell-diver brought up more mud, the tortoise supported it, until there was a firm spot on which the woman could rest. The ducks and beavers went on making the land larger and larger, and at last little red bushes, like water reeds, began to sprout. The sky woman was the foundress of the Seneca tribe.

The Algonquins have a very similar myth about No-komis, who fell from the moon and bore a daughter, who in turn was the mother of the tribe's Culture Hero (sometimes called Hiawatha); and the Hurons have a tale almost exactly like that of the Senecas. On the island formed on the tortoise's back, their ancestress is delivered of twins.

The Osage Indians of Oklahoma say that the Sun-Father and the Moon-Mother, from whom they and all other living creatures have come down, once fell into the ocean and rose from it with the help of the Elk, from whose magical loose hairs vegetation later grew.

Sir George Grey, in *Polynesian Mythology,* lets us hear Maui, the child demigod, tell the story of his birth to his divine mother. "I was born at the side of the sea, and was thrown by you into the foam of the surf, after you had wrapped me up in a tuft of your hair, which you cut off for the purpose; then the seaweed formed and fashioned me, as caught in its long tangles the ever-heaving surges of the sea rolled me, folded as I was in them, from side to side; at length the breezes and squalls which blew from the ocean drifted me on to shore again, and the soft jelly-fishes of the long sandy beaches rolled themselves round me to protect me." His divine forebear, Tama-nui-ki-te Rangi, unwinds the helpful jellyfishes and sees a human being, Maui.

Myths of this type remind us of the many stories of the world fished up by animals. P'an Ku, while shaping the cosmos, was assisted by four fabulous beasts: the dragon, the tortoise, the unicorn, and the phoenix.

Best known of all the animal-helper legends is that of the twins, Romulus and Remus, who were nursed by a wolf and later founded the race of Romans.

In one story, at least, the role of the animal helper is reversed. According to the Black Tatars of Siberia, the first human beings were created by the demiurge Pajana. But Pajana was unable to endow them with life-giving spirits, so he had to go to Kudai, the High God in heaven, to beg human souls of Him. Meanwhile, Pajana left a naked dog to guard the humanlike figures. Erlik, the devil, came and said to the dog: "You have no hair. I'll give you a golden covering, if you'll let me have these soulless ones." The offer pleased the cur, and Erlik had his chance. The devil

profaned the people with his spittle, which dripped and
ran over them. The moment he spied Kudai approaching
and bringing souls, Erlik took flight. Kudai saw how the
figures had been defiled, so he turned them inside out. That
is why the intestines of the human body are filled with
spittle and impurity.

Sodomy between man and beast is also very common in
these stories. Often they portray someone who escapes from
the flood and, left solitary, mates with something not of his
own kind. Perhaps the woman chooses a snake, an obvious
phallic symbol; or—as we have seen—a bird or a goat. An
Australian tribe, for instance, tells of a woman who marries
To Uvalum, the volcano snake. She gives birth to a son who
moves into a mountain where he still sits and smokes, spit-
ting fire and stones over the area. The natives trace their
lineage to this volcano god.

Kelsey, in *Seven Keys to Brazil*, has preserved this lovely
tale of Indians there:

> *In the time when men made fishing-nets of cane, a
> fisherman one day found three birds in his net—
> Jacamins—one yellow, one red, one black. Drawing
> his bow, he shot the yellow bird. Immediately, the
> waters began to rise and pour over the banks.*
>
> *The fisherman ran for his life; the waters pursued
> him. He ran and ran until he reached his village,
> seized a firebrand, warned everyone to fly, and ran on
> and on again. Some of his people tried to leave, some
> did not believe him; but it did not matter, for the
> waters swept over them all and raced after the fisher-
> man.*
>
> *At last he reached a mountain and climbed to the
> top. From there he could see nothing but water, and,
> as he looked, it rose steadily toward him. He cudgelled
> his wits for a means of saving himself and finally had
> an inspiration. Seizing his firebrand, he heated a stone*

red, broke it and hurled the fragments in four direc-
tions. The waters stopped rising and began to go
down.

When the flood was quite gone, the fisherman
descended and ran to his home. But no village was
there, and though he whistled and whistled, none
replied. "Woe is me!" he cried. "No one lives but me."
As he looked about, however, he saw the tracks of a
deer, and when he whistled again, a whistle answered
his. Following tracks and sound, he came upon a
gentle little doe.

He looked at the animal keenly, then said, "You
shall be my wife." From that moment the doe was with
him always. They had many children, the first a
perfectly formed deer, the second not so perfect; the
third was a son, half man, half animal; and others, as
they were born, more and more resembled human
beings. At last, "giving a whole day to his offspring,"
the fisherman mated them in pairs. And from them
came a new people to live in the world.

We notice that this Culture Hero is again a fire bringer
(his first thought is to take up a firebrand and salvage it
from the threatened village). And perhaps the shooting of
the yellow bird has reference to the sun. Such interpretations are always dubious, however, without fuller knowledge of the tribe's mythology.

The Cañari Indians of Peru relate that their forebears
were a man and a bird, an ara—which belongs to the same
family as the macaw; the Tepanecas, a man and a dog. In
the Arctic Circle, the Yukon Indians identify themselves as
progeny of a man and a she-wolf.

The demiurgic Coyote is the ancestor of the Chimariko
Indians of California. Escaping the Great Flood, he finds a
fragment of bone in his canoe. Wisely he saves it, and later
it changes into a young woman whom he marries; by her,

Coyote begets the race. Another tale of the Chimariko attributes the origin of human beings to the Frog, who comes upon the ribs of a person who has drowned. These fragments develop into a girl. When she grows up, the Frog marries her and has human offspring.

Now for stories from quite another part of the world! One of the very same sort has been collected by Frazer from the Land Dyaks of Borneo. An old man nets a fish, a puttin, which turns into a pretty girl. The old man takes her home with him and gives her to his son, and the Land Dyaks are their issue.

The Horse-Mackerel clan, amongst the Tshi-speaking tribes of the Gold Coast (Ghana) in West Africa, are also proudly descended from a man who marries a fish, a horse mackerel.

An amusing story is part of the lore of the Masai, another African tribe, and is set forth in a fascinating book by a French anthropologist. It goes like this: Three men visit the god Ouende to ask favors. The first says, "I need a horse." The second, "I need dogs to hunt alongside me in the jungle." The third, "I need a way to refresh myself." And Ouende kindly gives to each what he wants: to the first, a horse; to the second, some dogs; to the third, a woman. The three men set out but are caught by a long rain. While they are in the wet and dripping jungle, the woman prepares food for all three of them. The men think about this and say, "Let's go back to Ouende!" And they do so. All ask for wives. And Ouende gladly changes the horse and the dogs into women. The men leave. Now, the woman who comes from the horse is greedy; the women who come from the dogs are spiteful; but the first wife, given by Ouende to the man who asked to be refreshed, is good; and she is the mother of the human race.

Countless numbers of other stories tell of the descent of

man wholly from a totem animal. No mating with a human is suggested.

In the first chapter of this book, I quoted the legend of the Shilluk, in the Sudan, who declare that they owe their beginning to the Sacred White Cow of the Nile. It is a typical totem myth of this kind.

The Wanika, in East Africa, think that they come from the hyena. Another sacred animal in Africa, often named as an ancestor, is the hippopotamus. Beauty and grace are obviously not the criteria when primitive people select an animal forebear. In Madagascar, some of the Malagasy claim that the first of their line was a large lemur. A different tribe on Madagascar, the Betsimisaraka, say that they are from the aye-aye, a slothlike creature whose hind feet are shaped like hands. The choice of the totem ancestor is partly influenced by the locality, the type of animal that lives there. But not entirely. Still another tribe in Madagascar has chosen the babacoote. Why does one tribe on the same island choose the lemur, another the aye-aye, and a third the related babacoote?

Central Asia provides us plenty of tales in the same vein. Long before Darwin, the Tibetans believed that a kindly mountain god had evolved man from the chattering monkey. The leopard is given the honor of their source by other simple people in Asia. When a leopard is found dead of natural causes in the thick jungle, it is buried with the solemn funeral rites accorded humans. On Sumatra, a clan in Mandailing boast that they owe their existence to a fecund tiger.

The Pacific Islands yield a variety of examples, some of which may startle the sober reader. The Battas, of central Sumatra, have a range of totem forebears: apes, cats, white buffaloes, goats, and turtledoves. Throughout the Malayan archipelago, totem practices and traditions are equally prevalent. Separate clans of the Amboinese pay their respect and homage to the pig, the octopus, the shark, the eel, and others. In Ceram, serpents and iguanas are deemed ancestral; and, in the South Pacific, the Fiji Islanders speak of the rat as "our father."

The Dieri, of Western Australia, tell a curious story:

> *One early morning, from a fissure in the midst of Perigundi Lake, came forth the crow, the shell parakeet, and the emu. These birds lay weakly in the wet sand, until the sun infused them with vital heat, and at last they changed into men and rose up and dispersed to every quarter.*

Still other Dieri say that they are the progeny of black lizards. Paralina, a Mura-mura, took it upon himself to reshape these lizards rather drastically: he lopped off their tails, then gave them a nose, human eyes, and a mouth and ears. Waterfowl, such as swans and ducks, are the creatures to which some other Australian aborigines trace their strain.

Malinowski informs us that the Trobriand Islanders are divided into four clans, named after their ancestors, in the order in which they came out of a hole in the ground: the Lukulabuta clan, for the iguana, which scratched its way out first, in typical iguana fashion, then climbed a tree to watch the others; the Lukuba, for the dog; the Malasi, for the pig; and the Lukwasisiga, for the opossum, the last and ever the lowliest.

Frazer, who has collected most of these tales, says that the Cassowary clan in Maboiag, in the Torres Straits, credit themselves with having inherited the cassowary's characteristics. They have long legs and can run faster and are bolder than other people.

Amongst South American Indians, the odd pattern is the same. The Bororos of Brazil make no distinction between themselves and their tribal bird ancestor; they simply think of themselves as red-plumaged parrots.

The Piaroas of the Orinoco are not only descended from the hoofed tapir (a strange cross between a hog and a rhinoceros), but look forward to being tapirs again when they die. The Canelos of the steamy regions of Ecuador are destined to become jaguars, because that is what they were before. Some Peruvian jungle tribesmen were once pumas, and others in the higher altitudes were originally condors. I have already recounted in my first chapter the beautiful *Genesis* of the Aymara of Bolivia, who are the children of the Eagle Men, an appropriate choice for people who live in the thin air of that high land.

North American Indians are the most totemistic of all. The Delaware are the offshoots of the rattlesnake. The Crane clan of the Ojibways owes its being to a pair of fond cranes.

Once a male snail was stranded, high and dry, on the banks of the Missouri River by receding floodwaters. The sunlight ripened it into a man, who met a virgin beaver maid and wed her. This union brought forth the Osages. And the Carp clan of the Ootawak have sprung up from the carp roe, which also was warmed to human form in the sun. The Crawfish band of the Chocktaws owe their being to crawfish who rose from underground mud.

All these remind us of the Western Australian stories, especially the legend recounted a few paragraphs before this. So does the following whimsical myth:

> *A pool began to dry up when the sun became too hot. One very fat mud turtle, hurrying to find refuge in another pond, grew very warm in the sun's torrid rays. The turtle heaved off his heavy covering shell and soon after was changed into a man, the first Iroquois of the Turtle clan.*

The Haida, of the Canadian Queen Charlotte Islands, far to the north, are the offshoots of an encounter between a male raven and a mollusk on a beach. The mollusk gave birth to a female child, whom the amorous raven married, and from that double union came forth human beings.

By now, the reader will probably feel he has heard enough of these tales. I shall refer quickly to only three more. The Hopi and the Zuñi, in the southwestern United States, assert that all their clans have been sired by animals, and at death each man reverts to the form of his particular totem, turning back into a bear, or a deer, or a snake. The Black Shoulder clans of the Omaha had for their fore-fathers a herd of shaggy buffaloes who first lived under water. When a member of the clan neared death, he was wrapped in a buffalo skin to prepare him for his transformation; that is a perfect example of totemistic belief.

II

We can define totemism more easily than we can explain it. It is primitive man's feeling about a sacred beast, fish, bird, or even nut or fruit, which may not be killed or eaten by the tribe. Or, if food is very scarce and the totem *is* eaten, it can only be at a ritual feast. The totem is sacred, because it is the tribal ancestor. Or elsewhere it may be looked upon instead as a dead relative reincarnated. Or still elsewhere it may be considered the soul mate of an individual tribesman, a vital part of himself, an alter ego. The significance of the totem differs, thus, from one primitive culture to another.

Many a savage is fearfully convinced that if the animal sharing his soul should die, he himself must die; and instances are known where shock and fright have apparently brought this to pass.

Similarly, on those ceremonious occasions when the tribal

totem is eaten, it is believed that a transfer of the animal's powers takes place. In dances, at these feasts, the celebrants wear masks of the totem and imitate its characteristic behavior. This usually happens once a year at fertility-resurrection rites. Eating the totem allows the tribesmen to absorb its qualities. Frazer suggests that the Christian ritual of eating the wafer and drinking the wine, symbols of the body and blood of the Saviour, is a later form of eating the totem.

The attempts to account for totemism have been many and astonishing. As a world-wide phenomenon amongst primitive people, it particularly challenged the interest of Sigmund Freud. In *Totem and Taboo,* Freud asserts—in consistency with the rest of his theory—that such veneration or respect for the animal is an expression of the savage's ambivalent feelings, mostly sexual, toward the Primal Father. The son is jealous and fearful of him, yet feels guilty. Symbolically, he murders the Father and eats him, partaking of his virile qualities. The ritual is thus an hallucinatory satisfaction, an outlet for the son's repressed feelings. To "prove" this, Freud makes much of his discovery in psychoanalysis that children who pretend to be frightened by "wicked animals" often are actually afraid of their fathers.

Otto Rank, long a Freudian but later a dissident, has a very different theory. He draws examples from primitive ritual to show that aborigines often create animal symbols for the womb. So that it is not hatred of the father which motivates totemism, but instead an emotional need to find shelter again in the mother. He cites the "monster-myths," such as that of Tiāmat, the Mother-Dragon, as an illustration of this. He describes African burial customs that include sewing up the dead king of the tribe in an animal skin, as an instance of another symbolic return to the womb. This theory is at least as ingenious as Freud's, but it does not take account of many exceptions.

Whether one should accept either of these two explanations is not for me to say. I, for one, find them rather farfetched, though in general I have deep respect for the work of Freud and Rank. But here, I think, they are very wide of the mark.

Sober anthropologists try to trace totemism back to man's observation that worms, maggots, and carrion-eating birds and beasts devour the decaying corpse, which to a savage mind means that the animals also assimilate the souls of their victims. Once having become persuaded that his soul will go into the worms or animals who will some day feast on him, primitive man "inverts" the idea. He decides that he has *come* from those animals, too. Conceivably, he might find some comfort in the thought.

A good myth exampling this is the creation saga of the Samoans and Tonga Islanders, as reported by both Schirren and Buck. The god Tangaroa dispatches his daughter Tuli to earth in the guise of a snipe. Worms and maggots swarm out of a rotting vine, and the bird Tuli chips them into human shape with her sharp beak.

Joseph Campbell has yet another view and describes totemism as expressive of a search for kinship or brotherhood with the animal world, by which man, claiming to be blood cousin of some species, is its protector and in turn is protected by the animal wisdom of the wood folk. "For the primitive hunting peoples of those remotest human millenniums when the sabre-tooth tiger, the mammoth, and the lesser presences of the animal kingdom were the primary manifestations of what was alien—the source at once of danger, and of sustenance—the great human problem was to become linked psychologically to the task of sharing the wilderness with these beings. An unconscious identification took place, and this was finally rendered conscious in the half-human, half-animal figures of the mythological totem-ancestors. The animals became the tutors of humanity. . . . Similarly, the tribes supporting themselves on plant-food became cathected to the plant, the life-rituals of planting and reaping were identified with those of human procreation, birth, and progress to maturity."

This theory, it seems to me, is more imaginative than that of the conventional anthropologists; and yet, in its human simplicity, more sound and plausible than that of the Freudians, who sometimes ascribe overcomplexity to primitive motivations.

In Campbell's opinion, early man's seasonal festivals were more than mere efforts to control the forces of nature. He points out that there are none which seek to ward off the advent of the cold season, the winter, for example. Instead, these rites are symbolic of man's submission to his destiny, his readiness to endure it.

Campbell continues: "Both the plant and animal worlds, however, were in the end brought under social control. Whereupon the great field of instructive wonder shifted—to the skies—and mankind enacted the great pantomime of the sacred moon-king, the sacred sun-king, the hieratic, planetary state, and the symbolic festivals of the world-regulating spheres."

This accords with Everett's argument that some part of primitive man's desire to create heroes, nonhuman and superhuman, arose in him from fear of his own uniqueness in the cosmos.

We do know that historically the totem-gods come first, when people are hunters, and that a change to agriculture carries with it a human turning to vegetation gods. The anthropomorphic gods, those resembling man himself, come last. They appear in the speculations of the Sumerians, a people who probably once dwelt in the mountains near China, and later moved across India and the Persian Gulf, to establish themselves in Mesopotamia.

Man-shaped gods were also worshipped very early amongst the Egyptians, but usually the Egyptian gods had a combination of human and animal characteristics. Thoth had the head of an ibis or sometimes a baboon; Osiris often took the form of a bull, and his sister-wife Isis that of a hawk. Sekhmet had the head of a cat or lioness.

We find traces of totemism in the influential sky animals of the Babylonian Zodiac. The ancient cult of astrology still has a populous modern following, which little knows the origin of it.

Hindu deities, too, have many animal incarnations. Prajāpati, in his paternal strain, is sometimes represented as the boar. The boar is also the sacred beast of the Sumerian Tammuz, who later becomes Adonis, in some aspects of his history a predecessor to the Christian Saviour. The Chinese have a masculine boar-god, Chu Pa-Chieh, Lord of the Milky Way, who rapes the daughter of the sky. In his form as a boar, Prajāpati raises the earth from the sea. Later, in one of his manifestations, the divine Prajāpati becomes Rudra, again the boar of heaven, the creator of the world.

Another favorite totem-god is the tortoise. When Prajāpati wants to have offspring, he becomes a tortoise, the Lord of the Waters. The Chinese Lord of the Waters is also a tortoise. In another Hindu legend, the world rests on the back of a tortoise, a manifestation of Vishnu. We are reminded of the American Indian myth, so poetically told by the Senecas and Hurons, of the New World resting on the back of a tortoise, while the tribe is propagated. Is there any connection between the Asian and American myths? Kerényi remarks that the tortoise is such a primeval-looking monster that even the youngest one could, by the looks of it, be described as the most ancient creature of the world. Kaçyapa, considered by some the father of the first Hindu gods, is known as the "tortoise-man."

Perhaps the most prevalent totemistic idea, held by millions today, is the active Hindu belief in the transmigration of the soul. After one's death, the rebirth of one's soul is possible in another body of either human or animal form.

11

FROM MAGIC CLAY

One of the oldest myths about the origin of man, the Sumerian, has only recently been discovered and translated.

The Goddess of the Primeval Sea, like the other deities, is tired of having to work for her daily food. Why not use clay to fashion a race of men who can serve the gods? Then they need never work any more.

The heavenly clan carry out their task at a drunken banquet. Nimnah, Mother Earth, tries her hand and shapes six unsuccessful types of human beings: one is a woman who cannot give birth, and another a creature who is sexless. Enki, God of the Sea and Wisdom, grows angry at these failures and takes the clay in his fingers but turns out a human creature weak in body and spirit, which explains why the world is filled with misfits. This still does not satisfy the inebriated gods, and a long dispute follows, after which the creation of man is finally accomplished.

It is hardly a flattering image of the gods or the destiny of man, given by the Sumerians. Yet in the next millennium, the Babylonians say that man was created by Marduk, with the help of Ea, for the same reason, to serve the heavenly ones, that the gods might rest.

The Hebrew *Genesis* seems to borrow from the Sumero-Babylonian epics, except that God ordains man in a more disinterested spirit, through "pure philanthropy, or possibly to mitigate His endless isolation." The Hebrews' man, too, is made of clay, or magical mud, and his name, Adam, is a form of the Hebrew word *adamah*, "earth."

One Egyptian story says that Khnemu, the father of the gods, molded men of clay on a potter's wheel. (To illustrate the complexity of Egyptian myth, we should explain that its creation deities include the feminine Neith and the androgynous Nekhebet; the latter, an avatar or manifestation of Neith, is called the "father of fathers and mother of mothers." Nekhebet existed from before the dawn of time and shaped the world. But then, in the Egyptian pantheon, the bisexual Nekhebet gives way to the completely male Khnemu—also known as Khnoumou and Khenemu-Shu—who is self-conceived and begets the gods and humankind. Besides this, there are Khepri, the Morning Sun, who has already been mentioned and shall be referred to again; and later Ptah, and Aton.)

II

Myths of man's clay origin, by Frazer's count, are quite as widespread as the totemistic ones.

Frazer opens his summary of them by saying that Prometheus is acknowledged by the Greeks as the original fashioner in clay of man, woman, and the beasts. This creation occurred in a little glen below the hillside of Panopeus, though sometimes it is purported to have been at Iconium in Lycanonia.

Other Greek variants abound, however, in poetry and legendry. In most of them, the primordial male springs directly from Earth. Each locality has its own story about this event. In one, the first man to appear on earth is Alalkomeneus, by the shores of Lake Kopais in Boeotia; in another, it is Pelasgus of Arcadia, who had being even before the moon; a third is about Dysaules, of Eleusis; and a fourth about Kabeiros, of Lemnos. In Argos, Phoroneus is the founder, Culture Hero, and Fire Thief.

Early races of men, who might have been the very first, are the priestly Idaean Curetes in Crete; and the Phrygian Corybantes, who were the original men "seen by the Sun God when they shot up like trees." And, of course, the Athenians later claimed that their beloved Attica had given birth to man. Indeed, so pure was the Attic soil that it yielded no wild beasts, but only a human being "who surpasses all others in reason and alone worships justice and gods."

The tale of Prometheus, moreover, has many versions, amongst them those related by Hesiod and Protagoras. One tells how Prometheus fashioned a First Man of irresistible beauty and kept him hidden, because the Greek gods were notoriously bisexual. Eros betrayed the secret to Zeus, who despatched Hermes to bring the handsome being to him. So enamoured was Zeus, that he gave Prometheus' creation the elixir of immortality to quaff, and the First Man now gleams in the sky as the planet Jupiter, earlier known as Phainon, "the Shining One."

Later, Prometheus shaped more men in the forms of statues of water and earth. Roman sarcophagi are adorned with reliefs showing Athena bestowing such earthen statues with a soul, symbolized by a butterfly—the Greek word for butterfly being *psyche*. Kerényi reports that in the region of Phocis, visitors were formerly shown huge blocks of a stone which were said to smell like a human body and to be left over from the clay of which Prometheus had fashioned mankind.

In another myth, the Greek immortals shaped the first man and his fellows underground, of earth and fire. Prometheus and his somewhat foolish and careless brother, Epimetheus, were commanded to equip men and beasts with all the qualities and gifts they might require. Epimetheus begged his brother to let him perform this task and improvidently distributed everything to the lesser creatures, so that man was left unprotected and bare in the world. Consequently, Prometheus was forced to steal fire, as well as the skill and art of Hephaestus (God of the Forge) and the quick wit and wisdom of Pallas Athena, to arm naked mankind for its travails in the world.

To punish Prometheus for this crime and an earlier offence, Zeus ordained the creation of woman by his lamed son Hephaestus, who mixed earth and water, and implanted in it a sweet voice and deceptive strength. The other immortals joined in the plot by adorning her; from Pallas Athena came gossamer white raiment and a silver girdle. Hesiod says that Prometheus was too wily to accept this gift from the gods, but Epimetheus, the easily duped, did. And in time this first woman, Pandora, let loose all the ills of mankind. Other half-lost stories state that Prometheus himself created Pandora, or even that Epimetheus did; and still others depict her as having risen from the earth as a goddess. Kerényi comments that her name, Pandora (or Pandor), means the "rich in gifts" or "the all-giving," which is a name also used for the earth itself.

To these myths of more sophisticated peoples, we might add that of the *Koran* which says that God created man of clay like an earthen vessel.

III

Elsewhere in Africa and other quarters of the world, simpler folk repeat even more vivid tales of the mud sculpture of man, who by some necromancy becomes animate. The Yoruba boast that they were shaped of clay by their chief god, Obatala, the sky deity.

The Fan, also in Africa, recount how Mbere, the Creator, took clay and formed it like a lizard. Mbere put this lizard into a bowl of sea water. On the eighth day, Mbere took a look at his work, and now the lizard came out. But it was a man. And, very politely, he said to the Creator, "Thank you."

The idea that man was once a lizard and lived in salt water foreshadows Darwin. The most interesting myth of all, though, according to Frazer, is that of the Ewe-speaking tribes of Togoland, in West Africa, who think God is *still* making men of clay.

In Asia, the Khasis of Assam and the Kumis of southeast India share legends about man's origin from impregnated clay.

The Dyaks of Sakarran, in British Borneo, have a creation story in which there are also the familiar animal helpers. Two large birds seek to make a man. They first try to use trees and rocks, but fail. Finally they choose damp earth and infuse the red gum of the kumpang tree into his veins, until life flows there.

In other parts of the Pacific, the Tahitians narrate that man has been fashioned of red earth by Ta'aroa, their major deity. On Mota, one of the Banks Islands, the creator is Qat, who uses red clay which he scoops up from the marshy river edge at Vanua Lava. The god Aulialia, on Nui Island, first designs earthen models, then shapes man accordingly.

Polynesian myths, according to Sir Peter Henry Buck, most often designate the god Tané as the artist-maker of mankind. The natives of New Zealand recount how Tané molded the image of a woman with red earth at Kurawaka. The mud figure was vitalized. Blood brought warmth to the limbs, her nostrils twitched, she sneezed and opened her eyes, and stood up. She is known to the Polynesians as Hine-ahu-one, the Earth-formed-maid, the mother of mankind. Tané mated with her and they had a daughter, with whom the Creator-God committed incest. The tale, with slight variations, is heard throughout the islands. In some versions, both progenitors of the race are human and earth-born, and the first male is named Ki'i or else Tiki.

The Tagalog story, in the Philippines, is a very familiar one. God carefully shapes a small clay figure but does not know how much heat is needed to bake it. Left too long in the oven, the image comes out burned black. This is the Negro. The next figure is underbaked and comes out pasty white. The Caucasian. The third time God takes His clay from the oven at exactly the right moment, when it is a lovely warm brown. So the brown man, the Malay and Filipino, begins his career by pleasing God.

In California, the Acagchemem Indians are in a long line from wet earth impregnated by Chinigchinich, a demiurge, on a lake bank; and the Salinan Indians, from mud brought up by a diving bird from the deluge and shaped by the Eagle; once again, the animal helpers appear.

Grinnell has recorded this attractive tale of the Blackfeet of Montana:

Old Man was travelling about; he was making people and arranging things. He came from the south, travelling north, making animals and birds as he passed along. He made the mountains, prairies, timber, and brush first. So he went along, travelling northward, making things as he went, putting rivers here and there, and waterfalls in them, putting colour here and there in the ground—fixing up the world as we see it today. He made the Milk River (the Teton) and crossed it, and, being tired, went up on a hill and lay down to rest.

As he lay on his back, stretched out on the ground, with arms extended, he marked himself out with stones—the shape of his body, head, legs, arms, and everything. There you can see those rocks today. After he had rested, he went on northward . . . and with some of the rocks he carried with him he built the Sweet Grass Hills. . . .

One day Old Man determined that he would make a woman and a child so he formed them both—the woman and her son—of clay. After he had moulded the clay in human shape, he said to the clay, "You must be people," and then he covered it up and left it, and went away. The next morning he went to the place and took the covering off, and saw that the clay shapes had changed a little. The second morning there was still more change, and the third still more. The fourth morning he went to the place, took the covering off, looked at the images, and told them to rise and walk; and they did so. They walked to the river with their Maker, and then he told them that his name was Na'pi, Old Man.

As they were standing by the river, the woman said to him, "How is it? Will we always live, will there be no end to it?" He said: "I have never thought of that. We will have to decide it. I will take this buffalo chip and throw it in the river. If it floats, when people die, in four days they will become alive again; they will die for only four days. But if it sinks, there will be an end to them." He threw the chip in the river, and it floated.

The woman turned and picked up a stone, and said: "No, I'll throw this stone in the river; if it floats, we will always live; if it sinks people must die, that they may always be sorry for each other." The woman threw the stone into the water, and it sank.

"There," said the Old Man, "you have chosen. There will be an end to them."

We see here that, as in the stories of Pandora and Eve, woman is responsible for the ills of human life, though the impulse of this ancestress of the Blackfeet is truly compassionate. But woman, it seems to have been the judgment of the mythmakers, is never content; she will never leave well enough alone.

IV

The Peruvian Indians of Tiahuanaco tell how, after a deluge, the Creator not only fashioned men and women anew, but also painted their dresses, and to some he gave haircuts. One man of each tribe or nation was produced in this manner. Next the Creator ordered them to pass *under the earth* and to come up in their preordained places.

Here is another persistent theme: many myths of the origin of man depict his first dwelling place as chthonian; he rises from an underworld darkness into a world of light. In some of these legends, man is not actually formed of clay; instead his coming up from the earth would seem to be allegorical. That he appears from the belly of the Earth, which is so often identified in cosmic myth as the Mother-Goddess, is significant to the Freudians, of course. Another feature of these myths is that the earth—or sometimes the cosmos—is pictured as divided into strata or levels, which the human race in its history must climb, mounting upward from one stage to the next and always higher one. It is a vision like that of Dante and Milton.

In the cosmic egg myth of the Polynesian island of Anaa, three layers are disclosed when the egg bursts apart. On the lowest are Te Tumu and Te Papa, the male and female deities, who beget man, animals, and plants. When this bottom layer is crowded by creation, the people make an opening in the center of the layer above, so that they can climb to it, and there they settle, bringing up plants and animals from beneath. Next they make more room for themselves by raising the third layer, which presses too closely upon them; finally they penetrate there also, so that humankind has three abodes. In a primitive drawing of this world (reproduced in Campbell's book), the people are shown standing on one another's shoulders to reach the sky.

The Navaho saga, in the American Southwest, is a remarkable one. The creation god Begochiddy and various demigods and a dozen forerunners of men and women, together with their animal helpers, the Locusts and White Locusts, Ants, Beetles, and Dragonflies, live first in darkness underground and slowly ascend toward the light, with many fearsome trials on the way. In all, they have to mount through four worlds—Red world, Blue world, Yellow, and Black-and-White world—before they at last attain this one. It is also told in this great poem that earth is created four times; the first three times it is destroyed by fire and water: the Deluge-and-Fire myth, once more. An extensive tale, full of incident, the poem accounts for everything in the

Navaho cosmos: the rising of mountains, the formation and coloring of deserts. The origin of the other known Indian groups is described, even that of the Eskimos, indicating that the desert-dwelling Navahos had a wide horizon, indeed, together with a true and deep poetic instinct.

The Zuñi myth also has the creative pair—the Beloved Preceder and the Beloved Follower—beginning in a cave world, near the navel of the Earth Mother. They build a great ladder on which men and creatures climb by a series of higher cave worlds to freedom in daylight.

Here the birth symbolism is unmistakable. Appropriately, the second of the caves, the darkest one, is called K'ólin tehuli, the Umbilical womb; the third, which is lighter, like starlit dusk, Awisho tehuli, the Vaginal womb or the place of Sex generation or Gestation. In Awisho tehuli the various peoples and beings begin to propagate in kind apart from one another, until they spill over into Tépaha-ian tehuli, the Womb of Parturition, just beneath our present world; and finally they are led out into the brilliant realm of the Sun Father.

In a magnificent passage of the epic, we are told that these human beings are crouched over when they come out, some even crawl along like toads, lizards, and newts; and at first their eyes are hurt by the unaccustomed brightness.

An amusing story in this category is told by the Kabyles of Algeria:

> In the beginning there were only one man and one woman, strangers to each other, who lived not on the earth but in Tlam beneath it.
>
> One day for the first time they met at a well, where they had a quarrel, then a struggle, which ended by their discovery of the delight of sexual intercourse.
>
> In time this pair had fifty sons and fifty daughters, but again the two sexes were complete strangers to each other.

Their parents sent them upward from Tlam by separate ways. The fifty female virgins, very curious, climbed out of a hole in Earth's crust and gazed at the plants and demanded: "Who made you?"

In those early days, the plants could speak and replied: "Earth." The inquisitive virgins then asked the same question of Earth: "Who made you?" "I was always here," Earth responded.

The virgins then asked the moon and stars, "Who made you?" But the moon and stars were so high that they could not hear this metaphysical query.

At the same time, the band of young men was also roaming on Earth's surface; and, by a bouldered stream where the young men were bathing, the boys and girls caught sight of one another.

The virgins were shy and afraid at first, but one bold girl dared to approach one handsome youth. Soon the two bands were together, and like their parents they learned the joy of sexual intercourse, and the human race was on its way.

The ants, very obligingly, taught these simple young people how to raise grain, and the other animals helped, too.

A Greek myth relates that the first people on the island of Aegina crawled out of the earth not as human figures, but as ants. After the island goddess had a boy by Zeus, the son of this divine couple was left by himself on Aegina; he had no companions, and by the end of his boyhood felt his isolation grow irksome. Zeus heeded his complaints and turned the island's ants into men and women, who became his subjects. These were later the Myrmidons, a name that some Greek scholars hazard derives from *murmekes*, "ants."

In Malinowski's Trobriand Islands, on the other side of the world, the ancestors of the four clans—the Iguana, the Dog, the Pig, and the Opossum, as has already been mentioned—emerge from their previous subterranean existence by one special hole, called Obukula, near the village of Laba'i.

The Freudian interpretation of this emphasis on a chthonian beginning has been set forth. It is simple birth symbolism, as the Zuñi myth bears out. But Rank, for one, goes further than the orthodox Freudians. Consistent with his view that early man described the cosmos more or less in terms of his own body, Rank argues that this persistent idea of an underworld origin is based on an animal analogy and always precedes the idea of a skyey or "heavenly" creation. It is held by a people at a definite stage in their evolution. The sky origin is only accepted when man has attained his ultimate nature, when "the place of his soul" is in his head, and when he deems himself primarily spiritual and even bodiless. Before that time is reached, the earth's interior, corresponding to the female abdomen, is looked upon as the center of creation and hence is conceived of as the belly of an animal. What seems to contradict Rank, however, is that the underworld myths of the Navaho and Zuñi are highly intelligent, as well as extraordinarily beautiful; they hardly belong to a people at a beginning stage of culture.

In most mythologies, and markedly in the Mediterranean ones, the Earth-Goddess or Great Mother is the dominant figure. Kerényi, speaking of the Greeks, points out that if the origin of mankind is set on a particular island—as on Aegina, Crete, or Lemnos—the goddess of that island becomes the Mother of the whole race. Actually, it is the same Great Mother who appears on each island, though locally she may bear the name of the island itself. Her personality is alike everywhere.

In Asia Minor, this role is played by Rhea, who is known there as *Meter Oreia,* "Mountain Mother," or else she is

given a name borrowed from a local mountain. She is sometimes shown in fanciful Asian iconography as hermaphroditic, or many breasted. In Phrygia, she is called Matar
Kubile (Cybele or Kybele). Her cult spreads widely.

Greek mythology, in all its convolutions, pays her tribute.
She is the mother of Zeus himself and other Titans and
Giants. She brings to light the beings who are the ancestors
of mankind, such as Curetes of Crete and the Corybantes of
Phrygia. She conceives by herself, immaculately, expelling
her male helpers, as did her own mother Gaea (or Ge).
Amongst Rhea's daughters—in Greek legendry—is Demeter,
another Earth-Goddess, also the Great Mother. Essentially
this triad—Gaea, Rhea, and Demeter—are the same figure
with like attributes.

In every other part of the world this stays true, whether
the Great Mother is the Japanese Izana-ma or the Polynesian Hakahotu: she is the brooding, fruitful goddess, the
source of life.

The German philosopher and classical scholar, J. J.
Bachofen, sought to prove in *Mother Right,* written in the
middle of the last century, that mythology is pervaded by
echoes of this mother cult. The popular adoration of Rhea
or Demeter or Cybele or Isis helped to shape societies that
were mostly matriarchal. Bachofen cites, as outstanding
examples of such societies, the Egyptian and North American Indian; but others, of lesser extent, are found in Asia,
Africa, and Australia. (This idea is also taken up in books
by L. H. Morgan, Robert Briffault, Oswald Spengler, and
lately Robert Graves.) Bachofen makes much of a conflict,
during the rise of Hellenic civilization, between patriarchal
and matriarchal religions. He says that the dispute and
rivalry had an effect on most aspects of Greek art and social
life, and even colors the impassioned tragedies of Aeschylus and Sophocles.

In a matriarchal society, a man seldom knows his father; hence all children honor only their mother and share her love equally. It is a culture of greater humaneness and tenderness; this maternal tenderness is reflected—Bachofen suggests—in the facial expression of Egyptian statues, and in the turn taken by Egyptian myth. In a religion of this sort, men worship the underworld or "lower" gods; their deities are chthonian, because Earth is the Great Mother of all.

In a patriarchal society, the family and religious system is harsher and hierarchal, but it does represent—in Bachofen's view—an ascent to a higher and more authoritarian type of culture and civic order, in which the reign of kingly or man-made law is far stronger, and a virile sense of duty takes precedence over soft feminine feeling. The Father-God is absolute; he triumphs in the legendary stories.

Whether this is actually a key with which to decipher the contents of myth, or explain the frequent incidence of the "underworld" motif in the creation sagas, is hard for us to say. Like many German scholarly theories, it is brilliantly documented but sometimes overambitious in its claims.

V

Otto Rank's over-all thesis, however, seems to fit better to a whole group of legends about the origin of man which correspond to those of the mystic edict, where the world is brought into being by a word of command. In these, the magic mud is not the only necessary ingredient; something else is required. The God's spirit or *breath* is essential to make man vital.

An example: in Australia, near Melbourne, the blacks tell how Pund-jel sliced three broad sheets of bark with his knife. On one of these he stood some clay and worked it up to the thickness he wished. He carved models of men of this new mud and finally blew his breath into them. The myth of the Kei Islanders is very similar. Their ruling god, Dooadlera, also blows upon the clay figurines and this brings the gift of life to them; they become human beings.

The Natchez Indians of Louisiana refer to man's origin from mud animated by the breath of God.

The Shawnee Indians of Ohio relate the story of one old woman left alone by a deluge. While she is lamenting her doom at having to live and die as the last of her kind, a heavenly messenger comes to her. "Consider how man was first created!" She finds clay and with trembling, gnarled fingers kneads a number of human shapes, but the earthen effigies stand lifeless. Tears of disappointment well in the crone's eyes; and the divine messenger, seeing this, again prompts her. "Consider how the Great Spirit quickened the clay forms." The cunning old woman understands this at once and breathes into the nostrils of her puppets. Instantly they take on life. To this day the Shawnees revere the Old Grandmother for this act, and consider her their ancestress.

(The note of sadness, when man realizes that he is alone in the world, is one we hear over and over in the myths).

The Innuit, of Point Barrow in Alaska, give man a long history from clay inspired by the breath of a spirit called *á sĕ lu*. Other Eskimos say that when the demiurge Raven made the first woman of clay, to be a companion to the first man, the dark bird fastened water grass at her nape to serve as hair. Raven flapped his black wings over the clammy figure, which thereupon changed into a beautiful girl.

12

STICKS AND STONES

In a good many legends, woman is created later than man, and also in part or wholly from a different source material. Adam is shaped from magical mud, but Eve afterward from his bony rib. We have seen this distinction made in Greek and Eskimo stories, as well. Very often, too, as in most versions of the Polynesian epic, the first male is a god or demigod, but the first woman is merely human.

Often, woman's later and separate birth is apt to be from the bark or branches of a tree. The Melanesian myth, which was mentioned a few pages back, is an instance. Qat forms woman not of clay, as he did man, but of supple twigs.

Another example offers itself in the African Fan *Genesis:* Nzame, who is God, names the first man Sekume but does not wish him to be solitary. "Make yourself a wife out of a tree." Sekume does so, and the woman walks about. The delighted Sekume calls her Mbonwe. The Fan say, "They are the father and mother of us all."

Tree myths are popular everywhere in the Pacific. They may apply to the origin of both sexes. The Amboinese and the natives on neighboring islands believe that their ancestors were trees. So do the people of Lakona, in Santa Maria, which is another island in Melanesia. Some stories there have man deriving from the wood of the dracaena, also known as the dragon's-blood tree; and others from a different genus, the tavisoviso: the wood carvings were brought to life by rival gods who danced ceremoniously and beat drums.

The Melanesians of New Britain, according to Meyer, have a merry tale about To Kabinana and To Karvuvu, the primordial men. First To Kabinana goes off by himself, scales a coconut tree which has light yellow nuts, chooses two that are unripe, and tosses them to the ground, where they split and become two beautiful women. (Thus, in the same archipelago, we have many marked variations in the handling of the same theme.)

When To Karvuvu, his twin, sees the women, he is envious and wishes to emulate his brother. "Climb a coconut tree," To Kabinana tells him, "choose two unripe nuts, and drop them." Unhappily, when To Karvuvu does this, he lets the nuts fall point downward, and the women come out with flat ugly noses.

Later, To Kabinana carves a Thum fish out of wood.
Once more his brother wants to emulate him, but To
Karvuvu turns out a shark, instead. "You truly are a digust-
ing fellow," To Kabinana complains. "Now you have fixed
it so that our human descendants shall suffer. That big,
hungry fish of yours will eat up all the others, and people
too." (This story reminds us of Prometheus and his foolish
brother, Epimetheus, who is inadvertently responsible for
the existence of evil in the world. Joseph Campbell is
moved by it to refer to an East African tribe which solves
this vexatious philosophical problem by saying that although
God Himself is good and wishes to be kind to everybody,
unfortunately he has a half-witted brother who is always
interfering. And we are also put in mind of the tale of the
Blackfeet of Montana, of the busybody woman who hurls a
stone in the river that results in death's becoming mankind's destiny.)

Here is the tale of the Asmats of Dutch New Guinea,
according to Dr. Adrian A. Gerbrands: A great magician
wandered through their country in very ancient times.
Lonely, he yearned for companionship. He carved some
wooden figures and stood them up in a jungle glade. He
beat rhythmically on a drum, and the wooden statues came
alive. This feat is still ceremonially re-enacted by the primitive Asmats: they whittle human-shaped figures and drum
them to "life." Much of the Asmat religious ritual is closely
connected with the sago and mangrove trees, and the fat
beetle grubs which live inside them, which are eaten by the
natives; and the symbolic blood-red sap that flows from the
mangrove when its bark is stripped off.

The Yana Indians in California declare that Jupka, the
Butterfly, created their tribe by words pronounced over
buckeye sticks at Jigulmatu. The sticks stand up and become the first man and first woman and a lad, named

Hurskiyupa. Then more sticks are transformed into more Yana. This is both an edict myth and a tree myth and has an animal helper.

In the great Persian legend, the male Māsha and the female Māshyōi are discovered in a plant. At first they are all of one piece; their bodies are joined, so that no one can tell where Māsha leaves off and Māshyōi begins.

The primordial plant rises and grows into a tree, and with its flourishing the tree's fruits ripen into the ten varieties of men. (The symbol of the Tree of Life recurs often in Zoroastrian theology. We have already heard of the Oxhorn Tree and still others in the Persian cosmic myth.)

Ahura Mazda, the Wise Lord, speaks to the interlocked pair: "You are man, you are woman, you are the ancestry of the world, and you are formed perfectly by me; carry out my law dutifully, have good thoughts, speak good words, perform good deeds, and worship no demons!"

The Lord releases them from their leafy imprisonment and sends them forth from this Eden into the world, where their pride, alas, soon leads them to fault and sin. They fall into the clutches of Angra Mainyu, the Spirit of Evil. A curse is put upon them. But finally Māshyōi bears twins, which she and her husband devour. They have seven more pairs of twins, and these survive to become the different races of men and gods. (We have noticed before that the birth of twins is yet another theme which appears often in creation stories, including the Inca.)

Turn again to Greek mythology: Gaea brings forth a race of nymphs called the Meliai, which means ashes. These Ash Nymphs, in turn, beget a species of men—in the Bronze Age—who are known as the Melioi. These men are first discovered "lying between the ash-trees like fallen fruit."

The Norse *Edda* credits man's origin to the sons of Borr who one day find two trees on the sea strand. They stand

them upright and shape men from them; the first son of
Borr gives the wood carvings spirit and life, the second
endows them with wit and feeling, the third provides them
with form, speech, hearing, and sight. The first male is
called Askr, and the female Embla. They beget mankind,
and receive a dwelling place under Midgarth, the great
citadel prepared by the gods.

II

Stones, not trees, are spoken of as the primal matter in
other well-known tales. Again the Greeks say that following
a deluge, all men were destroyed, save only Prometheus'
son, Deukalion, and his wife, Pyrrha, who were anxious to
have children. Pyrrha, whose name implies that her hair
was red-blonde, was the daughter of Epimetheus and Pandora. Zeus told Deukalion first to cover his face and then
take up stones and throw them over his head, and the
stones Deukalion threw became men, and the stones Pyrrha
threw became women. In Zeus's edict, revealed through the
Delphic Oracle, the stones are referred to as the bones of
the Great Mother, or Mother Earth. The first girl born of
these stones, Protogeneia, is later raped by Zeus, whose
satyric zest for such affairs was apparently inexhaustible.

The Lithuanians also narrate a tale about the man and
woman escaping a deluge, who are too old to repeople the
world, though they wish to do so. Pramzimas, who is God,
counsels them to jump nine times over the bones of the
Earth. They do this. Each time they leap over the flood-
strewn boulders, a man and woman arise, nine pairs in all,
from whom the Lithuanians are descended.

The close parallel between the Lithuanian and Greek
myths suggests a direct influence (though one hard to explain); but five thousand miles distant, in another quarter
of the globe, the Arawakan tribe of the Maipuré in Guiana

say that the last couple who have taken refuge on a skyey peak gather the hard fruits of the Ita palm and cast them over their heads. The stony kernels thrown by the man turn into men, and the seeds tossed by the woman turn into women.

The Makusis, also of Guiana, tell how only one man escaped in his skiff from the overflow which their deity Makunaima sent down to punish the demon Epel. To re-establish the race, this Culture Hero hurled stones behind him, and these changed into human beings.

The Caribs, in Central America too, relate that their archancestor sowed the loam with rocks which grew up into men and women; and that sounds again like the Greek fable of Cadmus, whose army springs up from the bony teeth of the slain dragon.

We can travel further and collect such stories. The Fakaofa, on Bowditch Island in the Pacific, speak of mankind as the offspring of stones.

III

In Southeast Asia, the folk of Laos declare that an envoy of the King of Heaven used a red-hot poker to split open a supernatural pumpkin. Out fell the aboriginal Kha, somewhat darkened by the searing heat, and next more agilely the cooler and lighter-skinned Laotians.

Another source of man is sometimes ripened corn:

In the Navaho epic, the first people—predecessors of the present race—were ugly; they had the teeth, feet, and claws of beasts and insects. They were also unclean, with a bad odor.

The gods—Hastseyalti, To'nenili, Yellow Body, and Hastsezini—wished to have human beings fashioned in their own image, with graceful hands and agile feet like gods.

So the Mirage People observed twelve days of solemn

preparation; then, at a long ceremony beheld by all creatures, two ears of corn, one white, one yellow, were swathed
in a sacred buckskin and laid upon the ground. With the
corn were placed a feather from a white eagle and a feather
from a yellow eagle.

The wind came from the east and west, blowing both
ways at the same time, whirling the dust about the sacred
buckskin, while the Mirage People circled four times
around the objects on the ground. The tips of the feathers
were seen to stir. When the buckskin was unwrapped, the
ears of corn had vanished; a man and woman had replaced
them. The white ear had become the first husband, and the
yellow ear the first wife.

The Navaho explain that the wind had brought them
life. It is the wind which comes out of our mouth now.
When this ceases to blow, man knows death.

The Mayan myth, contained in the *Popul Vuh,* depicts
the loneliness of the gods, even after they have brought the
world into being by their edict. The animals prove incapable of worship, so the gods determine to make men.

At first they resort to mud, but these creatures are ugly,
awkward, stupid and crumble and fall down. The gods are
displeased and do away with them. Next they choose wood.
These men can chatter and reproduce, but they have no
minds and walk on all fours. Disapproving, the gods ordain
a deluge which drowns most of them, although a few of
these men, made of wood, escape and become monkeys.
This is why monkeys look like men. Finally the gods
fashion four men out of cornmeal, and these are wonderful
beings.

The sharp eyes of these first men can see to the world's
end. Indeed, they know almost as much as the bright gods
themselves, and they grow too proud and boastful. Wrath-
ful, one god conjures up a mist before their sight to limit

their view. From then until now, mankind has possessed agility, good looks, and emotion, but little wisdom. To these first four men the gods give beautiful wives; they can multiply their numbers, and their children become the Quiché.

IV

In Mexico, the Michoacáns have been created by their great god Tucapacha. Here, as in so many other myths, the process is one of trial and error by the deity. The first couple, made of clay, goes to bathe in a stream and the clay falls apart and washes away. Tucapacha tries ashes, but again with an unsuccessful result. The third and last time, he uses metal, and this no water can erode; so the shining, new people are able to wade in the swift river and wash themselves.

Hesiod ascribes a succession of races, too, to the early Greeks and all mankind. The first lived in the Age of Gold, which was even before the reign of Zeus; it was in the time of Cronus, instead. This blest race lived free from care like the gods themselves, without work. The flowering fields yielded them all they required and fed their rich flocks. They never aged; they banqueted daylong; and death came to them as quickly and easily as sleep. The men of that wonderful epoch became after death the good guardian angels who yet hover over us, seeking to effect human justice.

Next the Olympians created the Race of Silver, which was much inferior; these men resembled their golden predecessors neither in grace of body nor soul. They lived like children for a hundred years, before they grew up; they suffered through a brief maturity, then died.

The third race, fashioned by Zeus, was that of Bronze, and warlike. In this age, men had metallic limbs, weapons, and houses, and fought incessantly and fiercely, with a loud and deafening clash of brazen shields, until extinction finally overtook them all.

Then came the Heroic Age, peopled by the men whose characters and adventures are portrayed in Homer's stirring tales of Thebes and besieged Troy. Last and worst followed the present time, the Iron Age. Men are mean and dishonest, unfilial, impious, lazy and quarrelsome. "Would that I had not been born in this age, but either before or after it!" Hesiod laments, gazing about at his fellow creatures. "Man is envious, slanderous, disorderly. Or else poor, hardworking, and wretched."

13

THE SACRIFICE
OF THE GOD

A most unusual myth, collected by Frobenius, is that of
the Wahungwe Makoni tribe of South Rhodesia. I shall
quote it only in part, omitting some repetitive passages:

> *Maori (God) made the first man and called him
> Mwuetsi (Moon). He put him on the bottom of a*

Dsivoa (lake) and gave him a ngona horn filled with ngona oil. Mwuetsi lived in Dsivoa.

Mwuetsi said to Maori: "I want to go on the earth." Maori said: "You will rue it." Mwuetsi said: "Nonetheless, I want to go on the earth." Maori said: "Then go on the earth." Mwuetsi went out of Dsivoa and on to the earth.

The earth was cold and empty. There were no grasses, no bushes, no trees. There were no animals. Mwuetsi wept and said to Maori: "How shall I live here?" Maori said: "I warned you. You have started on the path at the end of which you shall die. I will, however, give you one of your kind." Maori gave Mwuetsi a maiden who was called Massassi (The Morning Star). Maori said: "Massassi shall be your wife for two years." Maori gave Massassi a firemaker.

In the evening Mwuetsi went into a cave with Massassi. Massassi said: "Help me. We will make a fire. I will gather chimandra (kindling) and you can twirl the rusika (revolving part of the firemaker)." Massassi gathered kindling. Mwuetsi twirled the rusika. When the fire was lighted Mwuetsi lay down on one side of it, Massassi on the other. The fire burned between them.

Mwuetsi thought to himself, "Why has Maori given me this maiden? What shall I do with this maiden, Massassi?" When it was night Mwuetsi took his ngona horn. He moistened his index finger with a drop of ngona oil. Mwuetsi said, "Ndini chaambuka mhiri ne mhirir (I am going to jump over the fire)." Mwuetsi jumped over the fire. Mwuetsi approached the maiden, Massassi. Mwuetsi touched Massassi's body with ointment on his finger. Then Mwuetsi went back to his bed and slept.

When Mwuetsi wakened in the morning he looked over to Massassi. Mwuetsi saw that Massassi's body was swollen. When day broke Massassi began to bear. Massassi bore grasses. Massassi bore bushes. Massassi bore trees. Massassi did not stop bearing until the earth was covered with grasses, bushes, and trees.

The trees grew. They grew till their tops reached the sky. When the tops of the trees reached the sky, it began to rain.

Mwuetsi and Massassi lived in plenty. They had fruits and grain. Mwuetsi built a house. Mwuetsi made an iron shovel. Mwuetsi made a hoe and planted crops. Massassi plaited fish-traps and caught fish. Massassi fetched wood and water. Massassi cooked. Thus Mwuetsi and Massassi lived for two years.

After two years Maori said to Massassi, "The time is up." Maori took Massassi from the earth and put her back in Dsivoa. Mwuetsi wailed. He wailed and wept and said to Maori: "What shall I do without Massassi? Who will fetch wood and water for me? Who will cook for me?" Eight days long Mwuetsi wept.

At this place, we might pause a moment to consider the first part of the story. At first glance, it might seem unclassifiable, but one soon discerns in it several elements widely common in other myths. The Lunar School, for example, might claim it for its own, because Mwuetsi, like so many other Culture Heroes, is the Moon (the Man in the Moon?) or comes from the moon. Mwuetsi, the Culture Hero, brings the gift of fire.

Since both the moon and the morning star are depicted as rising out of Dsivoa, the lake, which might also be the primeval waters or abyss, the theme of the watery birth might be indicated here, and the myth has been interpreted this way by some scholars. This may be somewhat dubious and farfetched; still, it is arguable.

Echoes of loneliness are most pronounced here as else-where.

> *Eight days long Mwuetsi wept. Then Maori said:*
> *"I have warned you that you are going to your death.*
> *But I will give you another woman. I will give you*
> *Morongo (The Evening Star). Morongo will stay with*
> *you for two years. Then I shall take her back again."*
> *Maori gave Mwuetsi Morongo.*
>
> *Morongo came to Mwuetsi in the hut. In the*
> *evening Mwuetsi wanted to lie down on his side of*
> *the fire. Morongo said: "Do not lie down over there.*
> *Lie with me." Mwuetsi lay down beside Morongo.*
> *Mwuetsi took the ngona horn, put some ointment on*
> *his index finger. But Morongo said: "Don't be like*
> *that. I am not like Massassi. Now smear your loins*
> *with ngona oil. Smear my loins with ngona oil."*
> *Mwuetsi did as he was told. Morongo said: "Now*
> *couple with me." Mwuetsi coupled with Morongo.*
> *Mwuetsi went to sleep.*
>
> *Towards morning Mwuetsi woke. As he looked*
> *over to Morongo he saw that her body was swollen.*
> *As day broke Morongo began to give birth. The first*
> *day Morongo gave birth to chickens, sheep, goats.*
>
> *The second night Mwuetsi slept with Morongo*
> *again. The next morning she bore eland and cattle.*
>
> *The third night Mwuetsi slept with Morongo again.*
> *The next morning Morongo bore first boys and then*
> *girls. The boys who were born in the morning were*
> *grown up by nightfall.*

We have here a very pretty allegory which might be called a kind of primitive science. A clear distinction is made between the origin of plants and animals. Massassi, the morning star, bears the plants. She does not do this by coupling, but by being lightly touched with oil from the ngona horn. But the animals are born in a different way, by the mating of Mwuetsi and Morongo, the evening star (who is much more bold and wanton). The plants are conceived chastely by the mere brushing on of a magical substance; the creatures as the consequence of the sexual act, with only the partial help of the marvelous fluid.

> On the fourth night Mwuetsi wanted to sleep with Morongo again. But there came a thunderstorm and Maori spoke: "Let be. You are going quickly to your death." Mwuetsi was afraid. The thunderstorm passed over. When it had gone Morongo said to Mwuetsi: "Make a door and use it to close the entrance to the hut. Then Maori will not be able to see what we are doing. Then you can sleep with me." Mwuetsi made a door. Then he slept with Morongo. Mwuetsi slept.

We have now the drama of man's disobedience. The woman has tempted Mwuetsi, and she is to be blamed for the ills to follow. We expect this sinful pair, like Māsha and Māshyōi in the Persian tale, to be punished and expelled from their Eden.

> Towards morning Mwuetsi woke. Mwuetsi saw that Morongo's body was swollen. As day broke Morongo began to give birth. Morongo bore lions, leopards, snakes, and scorpions. Maori saw it. Maori said to Mwuetsi: "I warned you."
>
> On the fifth night Mwuetsi wanted to sleep with Morongo again. But Morongo said: "Look, your daughters are grown. Couple with your daughters." Mwuetsi looked at his daughters. He saw that they were beautiful and that they were grown up. So he slept with them. They bore children. The children which were born in the morning were full grown by night. And so Mwuetsi became the Mambo (king) of a great people.
>
> But Morongo slept with the snake. Morongo no

*longer gave birth. She lived with the snake. One day
Mwuetsi returned to Morongo and wanted to sleep
with her. Morongo said: "Let be." Mwuetsi said:
"But I want to." He lay with Morongo. Under
Morongo's bed lay the snake. The snake bit Mwuetsi.
Mwuetsi sickened.*

*After the snake had bitten Mwuetsi, Mwuetsi
sickened. The next day it did not rain. The plants
withered. The rivers and lakes dried. The animals
died. The people began to die. Many people died.
Mwuetsi's children asked: "What can we do?"
Mwuetsi's children said: "We must consult the
hakata (sacred dice)." The children consulted the
hakata. The hakata said: "Mwuetsi the Mambo is
sick and pining. Send Mwuetsi back to the Dsivoa."*

*Thereupon Mwuetsi's children strangled Mwuetsi
and buried him. They buried Morongo with Mwuetsi.
Then they chose another man to be Mambo. Morongo, too, had lived for two years in Mwuetsi's Zim-
babwe (royal compound).*

Throughout, there has been much Freudian imagery.
The psychoanalysts might single out the fire maker used by
Mwuetsi, and the fire, between him and the maiden, over
which he had to jump. The ngona horn, we are told by the
translators, is a miracle-working instrument, able to create
fire and lightning, to impregnate the living, and to raise
and give new life to the dead. It appears frequently in
South Rhodesian folklore. So an interpretation of it as a
phallic symbol might be a mistake, or an oversimplification.
But the incest references, the father's relations with his
daughters; and the snake; and the murder of the Primal
Father by his sons, for his "sin" in continuing to sleep with
the Mother, are also typical. To some they will seem to be
scarcely disguised, and hence easily read for their true and
ambivalent meanings. This story, with its dreamlike fore-

shortening of time, has all the characteristics of a sexual reverie.

Even more, this African tale may sound familiar to the reader. If he looks back to the first chapter, he will observe that certain passages—telling how Morongo gives birth to the eland and cattle and other creatures—closely parallel similar passages in the Hindu creation story from the *Brihadāranyaka-Upanishad*. Is this mere coincidence? Probably not. Other themes in the Hindu legend, particularly the flight of the goddess and her metamorphoses into various animal shapes in her effort to escape the amatory wishes of the god, are also found in Greek mythology. I quote again a sentence or two from the *Upanishad*:

> She thought: "He shall not have me again; he has created me from himself; I will hide myself. . . ."
> She became a she-goat, he a goat; she became a ewe, he a ram; they joined and goats and sheep were born.

Very like this is the Greek story of the goddess Nemesis and her bridegroom, Zeus. Seeking to evade his fierce passion, Nemesis transforms herself into various beasts of the land, ocean, and air. Lastly, as wild birds—she as a goose, he as a swan—the two deities celebrate their union by rape. Another variant of this tale is the pursuit of Erinys by Poseidon. This Fury, too, transforms herself into the shape of an animal, hoping to elude her seducer. Both Greek stories and the Hindu hymn fit into Kerényi's larger category of the marriage of the reluctant Kore, the Earth-Goddess or Mother-Goddess, which is imagined as having occurred at the very dawn of time. The Great Mother does not wish to accept the advances of the divine lover, as again in the only partly different stories of Gaea and Demeter and Persephone. Fiske, as I mentioned earlier, has established that Greek legends owe much to Hindu ones, so that these mere paraphrases need not surprise us. But the appearance of closely related motifs (though hardly identical ones) in the African story of Morongo—the Wahungwe Makoni Mother-Goddess—brings out again how many resemblances there are in myth everywhere.

II

We come at last to the myths in which man is supposed to be made of a god. The Hindu legend, which we have just quoted from the *Upanishad,* depicts God as being lonely and wanting a companion. He is as big as man and wife together; so He divides Himself. At the end of this continuous division (to which we have only now referred), man and woman are born. They are, in consequence, divine issue.

An Egyptian legend of creation says that Khepri, the Sun God, shed tears. Men and women arose from the tears that came forth from his eye.

In the earlier Hindu myth, the Vedic one, when Purusha is carved up by the other gods to become the cosmos, the four castes of mankind are also formed from his parts: the priests from his mouth, the warriors from the giant's arms, the farmers from his thighs, and the servants from his feet. But a more significant version of man's origin is found in the story of Prajāpati, who is dissolved by the very effort of creation. Sometimes this is portrayed most dramatically by having one of his manifestations slay a second one, to generate life. He creates Death and then must flee his unfilial son: one half of Prajāpati is mortal—his physical hair, flesh, bone, and marrow—but the other half—mind, voice, breath, sight, and hearing—is indestructible.

In the Navaho epic, Begochiddy, the great and proud God, is the son of the Sunlight and the Day. He dismembers his sons, the Twin Warriors, in order to form instead the twin vital substances, the male and the female (the

Navaho Yang and Yin). Then Begochiddy breathes life into them.

Easter Islanders believe that the omnipotent Sea God, Makemake—part bird, part fish, part human—mixed clay with his urine to shape the vital, beautiful body of man.

Melanesians in New Britain say that To Kabinana and To Karvuvu, the primordial men, were fashioned in this way: "The One Who Was First There" sketched two male figures on the ground, scratched open his own vein, and sprinkled his blood on the drawings. He covered the figures with two large leaves, and after a time the original men took on being underneath the leaves.

In the Chinese myth, the dwarf-giant P'an Ku perishes— like Lord Prajāpati—and from his death and dismemberment flows the life of the cosmos. His lice become the earliest race of men.

The highest form of this concept is expressed in the Sumerian story of Marduk, the slayer of Tiāmat. Grieved by the barrenness of the earth, he yearns to make it fruitful and is willing to use his blood to vitalize it. When the clay figures are finished, Marduk cuts off his own head. From the blood which gushes forth, humanity and the animals and plants borrow life; earth blossoms. His is an act of most unworldly self-sacrifice.

III

An early Persian myth, probably derived from the Sumerian, portrays Yima as a fertility god. He brings increase to the creatures of earth by means of two golden objects, an arrow and a scourge. With the magic arrow, Yima pierces the soil. With the gilt scourge he strokes it, which causes the pregnant world to yield more life of all forms and grow to twice its original size.

Yima also weds his sister, Yimak, in order to produce mankind, and for this loses his godhood and is killed in his earthly, volcano-rimmed paradise by the serpent Ahzi Dahāk. (Newberry shows that there are striking likenesses between the tales of the Persian Yima and Yimak and the Hindu Yama and Yamī, and also the Chinese Fu Hsi and Nu Kua.)

It is indeed a lovely dwelling place that Yima loses, along with his life; for this mundane paradise is guarded from the wintry cold by the fires of three surrounding volcanoes and has special lights in the sky over it; the sun, moon, and stars rise and set but once a year, and each year is like a single day to those chosen to live in this Elysian valley.

A later Persian myth is about Gaya Maretan, also the father of mankind. For three thousand years, Gaya Maretan has the spirit of an ox. At last he is transformed into a tall and handsome youth of fifteen years, taking his human shape from the sweat of Ahura Mazda; and after a career of combat with evil forces, he is sacrificed. From his corpse the metals are alchemized: gold, silver, brass, tin, iron, lead, mercury, adamant. His seed makes the Earth-Goddess pregnant, and she bears, in the shape of a plant, Māsha-Māshyōi, the Siamese-twin ancestors of humanity. Once again we see the death of a supernatural being to assure the perpetuation of life. We also note another familiar element in this legend, Gaya Maretan's long incarnation as an ox, a virile beast.

This Persian story with its strain of totemism—like the other one, recounted earlier, of the sacred ox from whose semen, purified in the moon, one hundred and eighty-two pairs of every kind of creature are yielded—has a strong affinity to the better-known Greek myth of Dionysus, to which we shall refer again shortly.

IV

In discussing Dismemberment myths, it was remarked that early man frequently turned to the idea that the fashioning of the vast world involved the killing or suicidal self-sacrifice of a god or supernal giant. We now see that this is true in many tales about the origin of man himself as well as of the cosmos. The universe is formed of the parts of P'an Ku, Purusha, Ymir, Viraj, Tiămat, Ferraun, Yemaja, Izana-gi; and similarly, from the same gods or later ones, like the Aztec Quetzalcoatl, mankind is created.

In the stories of lesser fertility gods, celebrated by primitive peoples everywhere, the same pattern is seen. (This is the thesis of Newberry in his study *The Rainbow Bridge,* to which brief reference was made in a preceding chapter.) The fate of these fertility gods, who are apt to be vegetation gods as well, is usually that they are tortured, killed, and finally resurrected. From their suffering and rebirth, the race of man reaps great benefits: man's very origin or existence might be due to their sacrifice, or through it he gets help at a time of urgent need.

The rites honoring such gods were generally held in March or April of each year, and apparently they were allegorical re-enactments of the coming of spring and the rebirth of vegetation after the long "death" of earth between the autumnal and vernal equinoxes. Newberry's belief is that the fertility-and-vegetation gods were personifications of these natural forces or phenomena.

Man's hope was that by solemnly recounting the story of the god's creative sacrifice with masked pantomime, dance, and chanting he might win heavenly favor and make his fields more fruitful. Especially, he would propitiate the fertility god by mourning his legendary death and rejoicing over his ensuing resurrection.

But an expression of profound regret for the tribe's errors and sins during the year was also necessary. Therefore, the tribe would offer a sacrifice—often a human one—whose suffering in a sense paralleled the god's violent fate.

This sacrificial victim—or scapegoat—might even be the king of the tribe, who was thus called upon to die in a spirit of expiation for his people; or a royal son or daughter might be chosen to play the role instead of the king; or, conveniently, there might be a nonhuman substitute, most likely an offering of the sacred fruit of the tribe, or the slain totem animal. Hence, as part of the rites in honor of the fertility god, there would be the drama of the "Killing of the Scapegoat," which has been observed and commented upon at such length by Frazer. This was a universal practice amongst primitive peoples, who sought to escape the god's anger by this signal act of atonement.

Since totemism pervaded so many aspects of primitive thinking, and a killing of the sacred animal was often added to the ritual, the actual or symbolical eating of the Totem or Totem God might also occur, so that the participants could partake and share of its divine and outstanding animal qualities: virility, courage, cunning.

Newberry seeks to show a vital relationship between all these primitive beliefs and observances: the Dismemberment myths of the origin of the cosmos and man; the fertility rites and mysteries, with which are coupled the dramatic ceremonies and re-enactment of the god's mutilation, death, and rebirth; and the Killing of the Scapegoat and the Eating of the Totem. Combine them, and the connection of myth and ritual becomes clearer, and the mutations of myths—the many changes they undergo in time—are partially explained.

Naturally, the variations in myth from one culture to another are many, and the ritual practices born of them quickly differ in many parts of the world, but the basic premise is nearly identical everywhere. We must keep in mind, says Newberry, that the Scapegoat and the Totem-God are often one and the same: the king will not die but will be represented by a sacred animal or plant, which will be sacrificed or eaten in his place.

Even more important, from our point of view, is Newberry's second contention that the primal creation god and the subsequent slain-and-resurrected god are often the same figure. Beginning as the Sky Father or the animal ancestor, the creation god may reappear later in a people's myths in reduced or enhanced form as their particular fertility god. Or else the fertility god (slain yet reborn) is the creator's son, a new manifestation or extension of himself. Or, having first been anthropomorphic (human shaped), the creator later assumes an animal form, as when Prajāpati becomes the boar, as does Tammuz, too. This metamorphosis in the myth is perhaps inspired by the substitution of the totem sacrifice for the human sacrifice in the yearly sacred ritual.

The best known to us of the fertility-vegetation-resurrection gods is the Greek Dionysus, the favorite son of Zeus. To save himself from the jealous Titans, Dionysus changes himself into a bull, but the Titans capture him and tear him into many pieces. While his foes are eating his flesh, Athena comes and rescues the heart of Dionysus and gives it to his father, Zeus, who swallows it. Thereafter a new Dionysus is born, Semele being his mother. It was this death and resurrection of the mutilated god that the Greeks celebrated at their famed Orphic rites of mourning and rejoicing, to which Christianity owes so much. In particular, the Orphic brotherhood drank the blood of a bull, which they identified with the dismembered Dionysus, later triumphantly reborn.

In the legend of Dionysus, totemism is clearly present. So is it in the story of Mithra, the last and greatest Persian fertility god, the young deity who slays the sacred bull of increase, and in whose honor the rites of the *taurobolium* were held. In the *taurobolium,* very popular in the Eastern and Roman worlds, the god's slaying of the bull was mystically mimed. Mithraism is also a major source of Christianity.

Initiates to the cult of Cybele, the Mother of Attis, in Phrygia and Lydia, were placed nude in a pit over which a bull was slain; the gore of the sacrificial beast, dripping on to the candidates, purified them of sin and promised them a new spiritual and eternal life. The testicles of the bull, symbolic of his holy fertility, were then deposited in a consecrated vessel and offered to the goddess. Attis, her divine son, is another dismembered and fertility-and-vegetation god, who is crucified and resurrected, and who also has animal shapes.

A myth which Newberry does not mention, but that seems to fit in with his theory of the recurrence of the totemistic theme in beginning stories, belongs to the Kikuyu tribe in Kenya. When Ngai (God) first parcels up the world, he recognizes the beauty and majesty of Mount Kenya and selects it as his favorite resting place. He tells Gikuyu, the first man, that if ever difficulties arise, he should offer a sacrifice and raise a hand toward the mountain. Soon after this promise is given, Gikuyu finds a beautiful woman, Moombi, under a fig tree. He has her, and she becomes the mother of the Kikuyu race; but all their children are daughters, nine in number. To obtain husbands for them, Gikuyu sacrifices a lamb and a kid under a fig tree, smears the fresh blood on the bark, and faces toward the holy mountain. His wish is granted by Ngai in response. (This legend might perhaps have been included amongst those in the preceding chapter, as an instance of the tree origin of man, since it is implied here that the fig is the totem-fruit ancestor. But it is the killing of the lamb and kid we wish to notice now.)

Frazer's interpretation of myth as a later attempt to justify an obscure ritual seemed to us partly inadequate, because legends concerning the origin of the cosmos and man had no obvious connection with ritual of any kind. If Newberry is right, however, the great seasonal festivals have an added meaning. Such ceremonies started, most probably, as dramatic enactments of the world's beginning; only afterward did they become resurrection as well as fertility rites, and rites of atonement. With Newberry's contribution, Frazer's theory is somewhat rounded out.

Like many other controversial writers, Newberry often strains to fit facts into his argument, and some of his myth interpretations are tortuous, to say the least. But all are highly interesting. He is not content with the usual roster of slain or self-slain divinities, which includes Marduk, Adonis, Attis, Osiris, Dionysus, Odin, the Aztec Texcatli-poco, Prajāpati, P'an Ku, Izana-gi. He wishes to add many more, and does so by an ingenious reading. Whereas we have heard elsewhere that these deities sometimes first appear as Culture Heroes and Fire Thieves and Deluge Survivors and later are enskyed, Newberry claims that this process has often been reversed, and particularly in the *Old Testament*. He postulates that the Jews, when they became monotheistic, took seriously the command "Thou shalt have no other gods besides me." They humanized and represented as historical persons many gods and demigods whom they had previously worshipped and whom they had borrowed from other cultures, notably the Persian and Sumero-Babylonian, and even obliquely the Hindu and Chinese. Many of these gods, thus later humanized, were once fertility figures. The *Old Testament,* he declares, is an anthology of ancient and conflicting myths, many of which have a significance never guessed at by successive centuries of readers.

Abraham, Newberry supposes, was probably once such a heathen fertility god. His name means "Illustrious Father," and he went on siring children long after he was one hundred years old. The Bible hints that Abraham and Isaac were married to their sisters, which would class them along with Tammuz (the Phoenician Adonis), Osiris, Fu Hsi, the Hindu Yama, and the Persian Yima, all fertility figures, too. The Hebrew scribes alter the stories somewhat, suppressing many of the likenesses. The tale of how Abimelech takes Sarah from Abraham reminds Newberry of like narratives about the Persian Rustam and the Greek Heracles. And the same incident is told again in the *Old Testament* about Isaac. The totemistic sacrifice of the child Isaac in animal form—the ram serving as a substitute—is another instance of an enactment of the slaying of the god. It is very close to the legend of the mutilation of Dionysus—changed by his father into a boar, sometimes a bull—and Plutarch even tells us that the Jews worshipped Dionysus.

Newberry compares the story of Esau and Jacob to that of the Egyptian Set and Osiris. Even the descriptions of the two pairs of contending twins resemble each other: Esau comes forth hairy and red from the womb, and Jacob smooth and pale. Set is the fiery sun, and Osiris the cool, white moon. Osiris is a vegetation god, as Jacob probably was at first. There is also much obvious numerology in the history of Jacob, who has twelve sons—the number of the months, the number of bright hours in the day. When Jacob wrestles with the angel, whose touch shrivels a sinew in his thigh, what has really taken place? Has Jacob been emasculated like Attis, and has his struggle with the angel been a symbolic rehearsal of his mystic wedding with the Earth-goddess?

His son, Joseph, whose name means "The Increaser," is clearly a vegetation god—in Newberry's view. In being tempted by a king's wife, Joseph is like Siawush, a Persian, and Hippolytus, a Greek minor deity. Joseph has a coat of many colors: is this not the sunset? Many other fertility gods are also sun gods, including Mithra. Young Joseph is cast into a well by his jealous brothers, but the same tale is told of Trita, an avatar of Indra, worshipped by Hindu herdsmen as the sender of rain for their flocks and fields.

The rod of Moses, the Culture Hero and fertility lord, brings water from a stricken rock; it is very like Mithra's arrow. The Persian and Vedic Hero, Apām Napāt, is also rescued from the waters, as was Moses. Their names mean the same. Moses, who could not enter the Promised Land, is even more like the Persian progenitor Yima, who lost his godhood and died for having offended Ahura Mazda. In fact, Newberry has compiled a whole list of Biblical figures in whose lives there are incidents paralleling those of Yima. Like Adam, Yima has a paradise where he dwells with his Eve, the Goddess of the Earth, Aramaiti. Yima also has monstrous offspring, much as Adam has after marrying Lilith, by whom he begets only devils. (In another version of this protean myth, recounted a few pages before, Yima is married to his sister Yimak.) He is like Adam in being prompted by a serpent, Azhi Dahāka, and then committing an unforgivable sin, which leads to his being driven from his particular Eden. Like Noah, he is given warning by God of a deluge or storm and brings the animals together to spare them. Finally, like Abel, in still another version of the story, he is slain by his evil brother.

We have already seen that the Adam and Eve tale is very close, too, to the Persian legend of Māsha and Māshyōi, who emanate from a tree and become the parents of mankind. The *Old Testament* pair are first joined by a rib, like the Persian Siamese twins.

Noah, believes Newberry, is yet another fertility god. A

deluge hero, he is reminiscent not only of the Sumerian Utnapishtim, but also of the Hindu Manu, who is rescued by
Vishnu from the engulfing waters. Manu marries Idā, his
daughter, and starts the human race. Not only the Noah
tale, but those of belated childbearing—by the barren Sarah,
Rebecca, chosen to be ancestresses—are discovered in many
other mythologies.

Next, the "Book of Esther" is probably an Assyrian myth
only slightly revised. Mordecai is Marduk; Esther is Ishtar
(fruitful goddess of earth and love); and Hamon, in
Sumerian, is the Double God, or the Sun God, Shamash.
Once again, says Newberry, divinities have been humanized
and presented as historical figures.

Newberry is next engaged by the symbolism of the apple
in Eden. What does it really signify? Is it phallic, too? Is it
a sun image, a fertility symbol? More likely it is totemistic.
Many totems belong to the plant world, as we have seen.
Often in rites fruit was offered instead of an animal victim.
Heracles is the apple-god. So is Apollo, as his very name
suggests; and he is the sun god and sometimes believed to
be Dionysus, slightly metamorphosed. The token of sexual
love, for Aphrodite, is the apple. Through many racial
myths, even in the Norse *Edda,* the apple is the emblem of
revitalization or rebirth. Also, Newberry hazards, the fruit in
the Eden fable might actually have been another kind of
fruit whose name has been changed in translation: the
peach or the grape—Dionysus was firstly god of the grape—
or the crimson pomegranate, also sacred to Dionysus, and
the symbol of fecundity and growth. Plucking and eating
the pomegranate was the same as slaying the god, to assimilate his virtues. When Agdos, the hermaphroditic son of
Zeus, was emasculated, a pomegranate sprang from him.
That is how the fruit originated. Nana, whose name connotes Earth, picked up the strange fruit and hid it between

her breasts and found that she was pregnant. Her immaculately conceived son was Attis (elsewhere identified as the son of Cybele). The sin of Adam in eating the fruit could very well be symbolic of his devouring the young fertility god, as the Titans, Zeus' foes, did with Dionysus. All these myths can be linked, for the story of Adam and his original crime goes back to Persian and Vedic roots; as do the Greek myths.

Newberry's point is that in the Bible one hidden or altered creation myth follows another, and one fertility god begets another (so to speak), just as in all other early myth. The pattern is unchanging; on the surface it is complex, but fundamentally it is simple. The progenitive god is sacrificed; he too is the Scapegoat. As such, he is castrated or torn to pieces. Perhaps he altruistically commits suicide; or he divides himself in two like Prajāpati, and one part of him tries to slay and devour the other. The world is born of conflict; the Totem-god is eaten.

Without accepting all his claims and evidence, we must still concede that Newberry often argues plausibly. The motif of the death of the Divine Scapegoat and his resurrection is present not only in the *New Testament,* but masked in the *Old Testament,* as well. Earlier, Frazer implied that it is the universal theme in all cults and religions.

Why has our imagination always insisted on this story of the mutilation and death of the god, before his miraculous return and renewed career as a giver of life and salvation? Why has man so often demanded, it, even in some of his myths of the creation of the cosmos? God is dismembered, yet through that gives birth to a new form. Is it all an allegory of our own human life, with its suffering and its hopes for rebirth after death? Man's desperate dream of immortality?

14

THE LANGUAGE
OF DREAMS

Have myths any true connection with "reality," as Jung and Kerényi suggest? Is there vouchsafed to us, in such stories, a partial apprehension of *the world itself?* But that raises the always tantalizing question of what is reality.

"I dreamt last night that I was a butterfly," says a Chinese poet, "and now I don't know whether I am a man who dreamt he was a butterfly, or perhaps a butterfly who dreams he is a man." One of the most noted psychologists of our time, Erich Fromm, has used this apt quotation to express his own feelings, in his book *The Forgotten Language.*

Fromm explains the universality of mythical motifs by an appeal to what he calls "symbolic language," which might be described as the language of dreams. He also seeks, to some extent, a synthesis of Freud and Jung.

He rejects Jung's leading idea of myths springing out of "archetypes" whose meaning is forever elusive, yet his own view of primordial images is not so very different. Says Fromm: "There is no need to speak of a racial inheritance in order to explain the universal character of symbols. Every human being who shares the essential features of bodily and mental equipment with the rest of mankind is capable of speaking and understanding the symbolic language which is based upon these common properties. Just as we do not need to learn to cry when we are sad or to get red in the face when we are angry, and just as these reactions are not restricted to any particular race or group of people, symbolic language does not have to be learned and is not restricted to any segment of the human race. Evidence for this is to be found in all cultures. . . . Furthermore, the symbols used in these various cultures are strikingly similar."

What of the diversity which also characterizes myth? Like Kerényi and others, Fromm concedes that climate and topography are influential factors. Some symbols vary in meaning in different climes, and the eternal tales change some details accordingly. In the myths of northern peoples, the sun is usually a friendly symbol, while to some southern races in parched deserts it is logically a hostile one. Fromm sums this up in a brilliant and handy phrase: "We may speak of dialects of a universal symbolic language, which are determined by differences in natural conditions in different regions of the earth." In interpreting the myths, one must take into account where and by whom they are told. Even so, the variations are not great; the symbols may even be inverted, but, if so, their essential values and meaning are still expressed in the myth by other symbols which are their equivalent. In one "dialect" or another in myth, man's deepest intuitions are given symbolic voice, and the barrier of this local speech is transparent.

To understand the nature of myths, however, we must understand the nature of dreams. Although he pays elaborate compliments to the Master, Fromm finds Freud's theories to be of only limited value in this field. In contradiction to other psychoanalysts, who term dreams irrational excursions, Fromm profoundly respects the activity of the dreaming mind. In the symbolic language of dreams, he asserts, is disclosed a special wisdom.

Fromm argues: While we sleep, we are no longer occupied with shaping the outside world to our ends. We can do nothing. But we are also liberated, freer than when awake. The burden of work is lifted from us; and so is the need of wariness, the task of watching and preparing to master reality. We can disregard the outside world; we gaze at our inner world, and are concerned there only with ourselves. When asleep we may be likened to an unborn child, but we may also be likened to an angel unbound by the laws of "reality." In the realm of sleep, the "I am" is the only point of reference for our thoughts and feelings. Sleep and waking life are the opposite poles of our existence. Waking life is taken up with the distracting call for action; sleeping life is emancipated from it. We are less inhibited. We behold ourselves and betray our true feelings to ourselves. Consequently, we may claim the clearest self-knowledge in dreams, and at times a higher rationality, too, though it is mixed with a share of irrationality. We are at our best and our worst. "We are not only less reasonable and less decent in our dreams, but we are also more intelligent, wiser, and capable of better judgment."

Yet even what seems to be the irrational side of dreams might not be truly that, Fromm asserts. We are not bound by space-time limitations, and so it is proper enough to act differently in a dream world. "Sleep experience is not lacking in logic but is subject to different logical rules, which are entirely valid in that particular state." What we consider irrational in dreams is only so when we compare it to what could actually be done in a space-time world, but that is a false test. We have a right to foreshorten events and metamorphose appearances in dreams, for there we really have the power to do it.

This idea has been held by others. Philosophers like Socrates and poets and artists like Goethe and Proust have declared that man is often more rational in dreams than when awake, that he then has prophetic or predictive power and greater insight. This comes to him not in ordinary language but in "symbolic language," which is peculiar to the dream state but is also found in myths.

"Symbolic language is the one in which inner experiences, feelings and thoughts, are expressed as if they were sensory experiences, events in the outer world," Fromm states. "It is a language which has a different logic from the conventional one we speak in the daytime, a logic in which not time and space are the ruling categories but intensity and association. It is the one universal language the human race has ever developed, the same for all cultures and throughout history. It is a language with its own grammar and syntax, as it were, a language one must understand if one is to understand the meaning of myths, fairy tales, and dreams."

What weight shall we give to myth? Fromm's reply is most unequivocal. "Is it important to understand this language in our waking state? For the people of the past, living in the great cultures of both East and West, there was no doubt as to the answer to this question. For them myths and dreams were among the most significant expressions of the mind, and failure to understand them would have amounted to illiteracy. It is only in the past few hundred years of Western culture that this attitude has changed." In this respect, Fromm echoes A. K. Coomaraswamy, who regards myth as "the traditional vehicle of man's profoundest metaphysical insights."

It is chiefly in their metaphorical quality that myths are universal. "The myth, like the dream, offers a story which expresses in symbolic language religious and philosophical ideas, experiences of the soul. . . . In this the real significance of the myth lies. Of course, different people created different myths, just as different people dream different dreams. But in spite of all these differences, all myths and all dreams have one thing in common, they are all 'written' in the same language, *symbolic language*."

Fromm observes that the myths of the Babylonians, Indians, Egyptians, Greeks employ the same symbols as those of the Ashantis or Trukese. The dreams of someone living now in New York or Paris are little different from those reported from people living long ago in Athens or Jerusalem.

In his quest for "scientific enlightenment," man has come to consider dreams and myths to be plain senseless and unworthy of his serious scrutiny. Consequently, the symbolic speech of dreams is "the forgotten language" referred to in the title of Fromm's book. Modern man's loss of this language has alienated him from much that is within him. He has isolated himself from the most human part of life. Fromm holds, with Jung, that this is a cause of modern man's continuous anxiety. It also has its wider perils, for if people suppress their fantasy and dream life for long, it is very likely to burst forth in neurotic and destructive behavior. Recent years have seen such periodic psychic outbreaks in Europe, which have taken the form of a barbarism strangely at variance with our scientific culture. Hitlerism, with its distorted mythology, is a clear instance of this.

In his actual interpretation of dreams and myths, Fromm uses many Freudian concepts. He attributes to myths much sexual content, though he tends to minimize the Oedipal impulse and conflict. He strongly equates with Freudian analysis the speculations of J. J. Bachofen, who discerns in myth signs of struggle between matriarchy and patriarchy. This struggle is reflected everywhere in tales of the past, Fromm believes. He also accepts the factual basis of some legends. They contain, he says, cherished memories of the past and are not just products of the fantastic imagination of early man. Presumably the task of separating these many various factors would be difficult.

II

I have given an outline of Fromm's theory here not because it is a capstone of all other views on the interpretation of myth, but merely because it is amongst the most recent. Much of his book is provocative and stimulating, but the great value he assigns to his forgotten "symbolic language" may strike some as unproved, if not wholly unprovable. That dreams have a rationality of their own is demonstrated in his work, and that it is pragmatically rewarding to explore them and record them must be acknowledged; but that there is truly a "higher wisdom" in them is asserted by him rather than specifically illustrated; to me this seems to be simply a brilliant statement of Fromm's faith.

Joseph Campbell, in his oft-quoted *The Hero with a Thousand Faces,* has a point of view not unlike Fromm's. He too says that great psychological truths are hidden in these age-old stories which are so universal, but time has obscured them.

An eloquent passage in Campbell's book tells us what has probably happened to the once-potent legends. "In the later stages of many mythologies, the key images hide like needles in great haystacks of secondary anecdote and rationalization; for when a civilization has passed from a mythological to a secular point-of-view, the older images are no longer felt or quite approved. In Hellenistic Greece and in Imperial Rome, the ancient gods were reduced to mere civic patrons, household pets, and literary favourites. Uncomprehended inherited themes, such as that of the Minotaur—the dark and terrible night-aspect of an old Egypto-Cretan representation of the incarnate Sun-god and Divine King—were rationalized and reinterpreted to suit contemporary ends. Mount Olympus became a Riviera of trite scandals and affairs, and the Mother-Goddesses hysterical nymphs. The myths were read as superhuman romances. In China, comparably, where the humanistic, moralizing force of Confucianism has fairly emptied the old myth forms of their primal grandeur, the official mythology is today a clutter of anecdotes about the sons and daughters of provincial officials, who, for serving their community one way or another, were elevated by their grateful beneficiaries to the dignity of local gods. And in modern progressive Christianity the Christ—Incarnation of the Logos and

Redeemer of the World—is primarily a historical personage, a harmless country wise man of the semi-oriental past, who preached a benign doctrine of 'do as you would be done by,' yet was executed as a criminal. His death is read as a splendid lesson in integrity and fortitude.

"Wherever the poetry of myth is interpreted as biography, history, or science, it is killed. The living images become only remote facts of a distant time or sky. Furthermore, it is never difficult to demonstrate that as science and history mythology is absurd." Thus the great religions, including Judaism and Christianity, have been blighted, Campbell says.

One can hope for the rediscovery of enduring values in myth if men develop a quite different approach to it, he continues. "To bring the images back to life, one has to seek, not interesting applications to modern affairs, but illuminating hints from the inspired past. When these are found, vast areas of half-dead iconography disclose again their permanently human meaning."

How is this to be accomplished? We are urged first of all to consider the psychological analysis of myths. Psychoanalysis has shown that dreams are not idle affairs of our half-conscious minds but are revelatory; the properly trained doctor reads them as symptomatic of our true nature. The affinity of myth to dreams has also been established beyond doubt. Although Freud, Jung, Stekel, Rank, Karl Abraham, Géza Róheim, and other dissident analysts may differ amongst themselves, they already have in common a large store of principles and able techniques. With these, the ancient myths can be deciphered.

Campbell is optimistic about the results. "Through the wonder tales—which pretend to describe the lives of legendary heroes, the powers of the divinities of nature, the spirits of the dead, and the totem ancestors of the group—

symbolic expression is given to the unconscious desires, fears, and tensions that underlie the conscious patterns of human behaviour. Mythology, in other words, is psychology misread as biography, history, and cosmology. The modern psychologist can translate it back to its proper denotations and thus rescue for the contemporary world a rich and eloquent document of the profoundest depths of human character. Exhibited here, as in a fluoroscope, stand revealed the hidden processes of the enigma *Homo sapiens*—Occidental and Oriental, primitive and civilized, contemporary and archaic. The entire spectacle is before us. We have only to read it, study its constant patterns, analyze its variations, and therewith come to an understanding of the deep forces that have shaped man's destiny and must continue to determine both our private and our public lives."

But myths are not exactly comparable to dreams, he warns. Their figures or images arise from the same sources—the unconscious wells of fantasy—and they flow or have flux with the same freedom from space and time, but they are not merely the spontaneous products of sleep. Instead, the patterns of myth are consciously controlled to an extent. The myths, as employed by the early poets and priests, serve as a powerful picture language for the transmission of tribal wisdom. Campbell finds this so in even the most primitive tales: "The trance-susceptible shaman and the initiated antelope-priest are not unsophisticated in the wisdom of the world, nor unskilled in the principles of communication by analogy. The metaphors by which they live, and through which they operate, have been brooded upon, searched, and discussed for centuries—even millenniums; they have served whole societies, furthermore, as the mainstays of thought and life. The culture patterns have been shaped to them. The youth have been educated, and the aged rendered wise, through the study, experience, and understanding of their effective initiatory forms. For they actually touch and bring into play the vital energies of the whole human psyche. They link the unconscious to the fields of practical action, not irrationally, in the manner of a neurotic projection, but in such fashion as to permit a mature and sobering, practical comprehension of the fact-world to play back, as a stern control, into the realms of infantile wish and fear."

Campbell's feeling about myth is thus close to Jung's, but there is an important difference. Jungian psychology says that man needs to accept and live by myths, for he must constantly heed the beckoning primordial images in them. But Jung does not say that the primordial images in themselves have any other value; he even admits that from one point of view they are "nonsensical." They are one way in which we think, one way in which we behold things, one way in which *the world itself* enters our senses; but there is not necessarily a complete factual relevance intrinsic in this. Indeed, Jung states that the primordial images often defy the other evidence of our senses. When that occurs, we have two pictures of the world. We must either reconcile them, or, preserving their duality, accept both.

Campbell is more sanguine. He feels that man should be able to construct out of the myths a true and unified spiritual picture of the cosmos. For they contain man's supreme lessons of the past; they tell us how to live and *know*.

He writes: "And if this be true of the comparatively simple folk mythologies (the systems of myth and ritual by which the primitive hunting and fishing tribes support themselves), what may we say of such great magnificent cosmic metaphors as those reflected in the great Homeric epics, the *Divine Comedy* of Dante, the *Book of Genesis,* and the timeless temples of the Orient? Until the most recent decades, these were the support of all human life and the inspiration of philosophy, poetry, and the arts. Where the inherited symbols have been touched by a Lao-tzu, Buddha, Zoroaster, Christ, or Mohammed—employed by a consummate master of the spirit as a vehicle of the profoundest moral and metaphysical instruction—obviously we are in the presence of immense consciousness rather than of darkness. . . . And so, to grasp the full value of the mythological figures that have come down to us, we must understand that they are not only symptoms of the unconscious (as indeed are all human thoughts and acts) but also controlled and intended statements of certain spiritual principles, which have remained as constant throughout the course of human history as the form and nervous structure of the human physique itself."

This is not to say that the ultimate picture of the cosmos is to be found in myth itself: it lies beyond myth. To reach it, there must be a jump. This is a term well known to students of mysticism. Says Campbell: "The function of ritual and myth is to make possible, and then to facilitate, the jump—by analogy." Myth is but the penultimate stage of knowledge. "The ultimate is openness—that void, or being beyond the categories—into which the mind must plunge alone and be dissolved."

Here again we have a statement not of fact but of personal faith.

III

What are myths, then? Divine revelations? Works of narrative art, showing aboriginal man's poetic fancy freely at play? Chronicles from prehistory, partly or even largely factual? A groping primitive science? Cosmic allegories about the moon and sun, the wind, the varying light of the sky? Attempts to explain obscure taboo and ritual? Efforts to bring order out of the incoherent dreams of the race? Pragmatic precedents to uphold a clan's social status and daily rules of living? Projections of man's changing belief about the place of his spirit or soul in his physical body? Composite products of "primordial images" or "archetypes"? The superior self-knowledge of man acquired in dreams and expressed in a universally intelligible symbolic language? The means, by metaphor or analogy, for a mystical "jump" to faith, to a true knowledge of the cosmos?

We perceive that myth interpretation is complex, and made more so by the many highly diverse ideas propounded about it. We may find a number of them perhaps too mystical to convince us fully. Some may seem to be oversimplifications, and others overambitious. Too many claim to have the whole clue, not only to myth but to an intuitive answer to the mystery of the universe. This is particularly a tendency in the theories of Central European scholars, who often combine fact and mysticism.

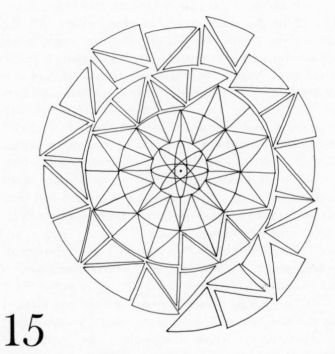

15

THE PRIMORDIAL ATOM

Like the primitive myths, the scientific hypotheses of
the creation of the universe limit themselves to a "beginningless beginning." Scientists never conceive of a universe in which is only nothingness; something is already in
existence from which the cosmos takes form. So the true
problem of the origin is not faced by any theory. This is

likely to be so, as long as physics assumes that matter cannot be created out of nothing.

One of the most widely accepted guesses today about the origin of the universe is that it began with the explosion of a single primordial atom. This is the suggestion of Abbé Georges Lemaître, a physicist at Louvain University; it was published in the third decade of this century. All the matter in the cosmos was packed into that single atom; other scientists call it "Lemaître's egg." Sometimes it is also referred to as "ylem" from the Greek for matter, and it is mentally seen as a "featureless mass of protons and neutrons." It was hot, heavy. Somehow it burst, "perhaps during the second microsecond of Creation." It exploded with enough propulsion to hurl most of its matter a billion light-years away. Future stars and whirling nebulae were spattered in all directions, while matter itself broke down into a succession of simpler forms; the protons and neutrons reorganized themselves into the ninety-two natural chemical elements known to us.†

We are reminded almost at once of Lao-tzu's vision of "the beginning": " *'There is a thing inherent and natural which existed before heaven and earth. . . . I call it Tao.'* The Tao has brought forth the one, the one has brought forth the two, the two has brought forth the three, and from the three the infinite complexity of the cosmos has taken shape." So spoke a Chinese philopher and mystic visionary who lived twenty-five hundred years ago.

A young Hindu physicist, Subrahmanya Chandrasekhar, has sought to compute the size, weight, and temperature of the first super-atom, which was filled with tightly condensed, subatomic particles. Its heat, suggests Chandrasekhar, would have been about eight billion degrees centigrade. A lump of

† The periodic table now lists one hundred and four elements, including twelve that have been man-induced.

it, about half the size of a man's thumb, would have weighed about half a billion tons. Mass equal to that of the present earth would hardly have filled a good-sized stone quarry. George Gamow, an American scientist, hazards that the whole of this pre-stellar atom was many times larger than the sun. Its density was a hundred thousand billion times greater than that of water; each cubic centimeter of space contained then a hundred million tons of matter.

Once again, we are led back to an image of Prajāpati emerging from the cosmic golden egg and then being quickly dissolved in the effort of creation. Science very nearly echoes the ancient Hindu allegory.

Lemaître describes the eruption, which let loose the swirling atoms, in these words:

> The atom world broke up into fragments, each fragment into still smaller pieces. Assuming, for the sake of simplicity, that this fragmentation occurred in equal pieces, we find that two hundred and sixty successive fragmentations were needed in order to reach the present pulverization of matter into our poor little atoms which are almost too small to be broken farther. The evolution of the world can be compared to a display of fireworks that has just ended: some few red wisps, ashes, and smoke. Standing on a cooled cinder, we see the slow fading of the suns, and we try to recall the vanished brilliance of the origin of the worlds.

We are still in time to have a glimpse of this once bright wonderworld, says Lemaître, for we have radium which has not yet been fully extinguished into dull substances like lead and helium.

The Abbé imagines this brilliant, heavy "cosmic egg" to have been a hot nuclear fluid; the proponents of the ylem, who came later—Gamow, Alpher, Herman, Omer, Enrico

Fermi, and others—assume that it was, instead, a hot nuclear gas. One of them compares the first moment of creation to the Biblical account of it, the "edict myth" in *Genesis:*

> *And the earth was without form and void; and darkness was upon the face of the deep. . . .*
> *And God said, Let there be light: and there was light.*
> *And God saw the light, that it was good: and God divided the light from the darkness.*

The Scriptures record that all the rest of the world-forming followed.

According to the ylem hypothesis, this is very much the way it did happen. The original explosion was a blast of light, and the universe rapidly took form. This dazzling burst of "light," as Gamow puts it, was composed mostly of high-energy X rays and gamma rays. Atoms of ordinary matter were as yet decidedly in the minority and were hurled to and fro by immensely powerful streams of light quanta.

Alpher and Herman have not hesitated to develop a tidy timetable for this whole affair. They have clocked the event to the last minute. Gamow, the mathematician, with whom these two American physicists have collaborated, admits that it sounds foolish to talk about something which took place billions of years ago and lasted only an hour. But he likens the process to that of a nuclear chain reaction in an exploding atom bomb which is over in a few microseconds. Years later, however, the radioactive fission products of the detonated bomb are still detectable at the site of the explosion; so it is with the uranium and thorium atoms in our cosmos today, several billion years afterward. We must, however, recognize that the scale of the explosion and the time following it is a relative one, as between our present atomic bomb and the infinitely vaster primordial one.

Thus it took only an hour after the master atom's explosion for all ninety-two chemical elements to be constituted in essentially their present relative abundance throughout the cosmos. In the first stage, a few minutes only, after a period which consisted almost entirely of radiation, the expanding universe was very dense and too hot to form anything. Within four minutes the radiation had lessened significantly and the temperature had dropped to a mere one billion degrees centigrade; the density of matter was about one-millionth that of water: all this allowed the capture of the neutrons by the protons in the particles' fast struggle to join up with one another, which resulted in the establishment of the elements. Simpler elements, like hydrogen, were formed much more profusely than more complex ones, like uranium, which fact accounts for their disparity today. The remainder of the first hour saw a continuation of this process, but the universe went on expanding and cooling for an initial ten million years. By then, the star clusters—galaxies—had taken shape, representing gravitationally stable gaseous systems. The mixture of matter and radiation had cooled to about three hundred degrees centigrade; the densities of matter and radiation were also about equal.

But what had happened to all the radiation which existed in space at the beginning? Physicists profess to believe in the law of the conservation of energy. Alpher and Herman concede that they cannot explain that. Some of the radiation was stored in matter, presumably, and is being reemitted to this moment, but much of it seems to have disappeared. The authors of this hypothesis acknowledge the contradiction and say no more. Astrophysical theories often have gaps like this.

As to what existed earlier than three billion six hundred

and forty million years ago (an estimate then accepted by this particular group of scientists as the approximate age of the cosmos) they modestly put forth no guess. In the beginning there was a boundless blaze of light and all other forms of electromagnetic radiation; our astronomers seek to imagine nothing more. Omer suggests that our cosmos is just a quick flash of light in the unlimited realm of eternity. It will continue to grow, but the accompanying law of entropy tells us that the inevitable end will be darkness.

II

Galaxies are huge clusters of stars, and nebulae are large clouds of dust drifting in interstellar space. Some remote galaxies may be mistaken for nebulae, because they are so far off that the aggregate of separate stars in them blurs together in one dimly luminous mass.

What astronomers tell us is that our sun and the solar system belong to a galaxy called the Milky Way. The Milky Way itself is part of a small cluster of thirteen or fifteen or maybe seventeen (and by one count nineteen) local galaxies of which the Andromeda Nebula and its two companions and the two Magellanic Clouds are also members. Our own galaxy comprises about a billion stars; some say ten billion, and some, since the use of infrared photography through telescopes, a hundred billion. Superior photography and larger radio telescopes, in the future, might reveal many more. The core of our parent Milky Way has been set at a distance of thirty thousand light-years from the sun. A light-year is roughly six trillion miles, so that the sun's position from the center of this encompassing cluster of stars is about one hundred and eighty million billion miles. This indicates the size of only one such galaxy, a small one, the Milky Way, the one we happen to be in. Our sun is somewhere near the edge of it, at the periphery, about two-thirds of the way from the core. In all, there are thought to be at least a trillion galaxies in the known cosmos.

The weight of the Milky Way has been estimated by undaunted scientists; but, explicably, the figure is forever being changed. It must be difficult to add up the weights of a billion or ten or a hundred billion stars, of unknown size, arranged in a galaxy several hundred million billion miles across. Some readers may wonder what a man feels, who wakes in the morning and says to himself, "I must get back to my work again, weighing the universe." At this very moment, however, an ambitious astronomer somewhere is surely doing it again.

One of the newest scientific "discoveries" is Hubble's, that of the expanding universe. Everything in the cosmos is in motion. Even while I am writing this paragraph, or the reader is glancing at it, we are performing part of a gigantic somersault with the earth, which turns on its axis once every twenty-four hours. At our latitude, the earth's speed in going about is nearly seven hundred miles an hour. At the same time, the earth revolves about the sun at eighteen miles a second. The movement of the whole solar system relative to the nearby stars carries us in the direction of Vega, in a third category of motion, at about twelve miles a second. The fourth kind of motion applies to the Milky Way, which seems to be slowly rotating at a rate between one and two hundred miles an hour, toward a center in Sagittarius. The figure for that is still under debate.

Hubble's rather startling suggestion is that there is a fifth sort of motion: all the galaxies are in flight from one another, from the center of the superuniverse to an unimaginable outer region. Lemaître's universe is still exploding, and in all directions. Our own galaxy, the Milky Way, is hurtling toward the constellation Draco, the Dragon, at a mere, relatively slow one hundred miles a second. Many others average a thousand miles a second. The speed at which the galaxies are dispersing—or, one might say, the rate at which the universe is expanding from its present known dimensions—is in direct ratio to their distance from us. A star group which is known to be twice as far from us as another is moving away from our telescopes at twice the rate. In brief, the farther the stars are from some center, their probable starting point (not the earth), the faster they are going. One far-off nebula has been clocked racing off at ninety thousand miles a second, which is nearly one-half the speed of light. So, many if not all of the galaxies we now see will eventually vanish from sight forever, beyond the limit of visibility, because their pace will exceed the speed of light, Einstein to the contrary. (According to Einsteinian physics, nothing in the cosmos travels faster than light.) Then no image of the hurtling galaxies could ever return to us, regardless of how much larger our telescopes might be constructed, even four hundred or eight hundred inches. Until recently, the *visible* universe, filled with its infinite number of star clusters and nebulae, was an approximate two billion light-years in diameter. Our finest telescopes penetrated no further into what lay beyond, but now the new electronic "image multiplier" has tripled that range, and radio telescopes can eavesdrop on constellations much beyond that. But with the galaxies escaping those bounds too, our heavens on future nights will be gradually emptier and darker and at last completely so, because the light rays and sound waves will not be able to travel fast enough or even practically far enough to carry images or signals from one retreating point of incandescence to another; there might be no stars in our sky.

Lemaître had contended, before Hubble's "discovery," that a universe of a constant size must be unstable. The slightest disturbance, even a sneeze, might set the whole cosmos to expanding—this is the picturesque way in which such an imagined state of affairs has been described. Einstein was finally forced to recognize this problem and attempt an answer to it. Hubble's assumption that the cosmos *is* expanding, in fact, fits in neatly with Lemaître's view. Einstein's attempted solution, too complicated to be detailed here, then becomes outmoded and needless. Our knowledge of the stars comes mostly from capturing their light, passing it through a prism, and then studying their spectra—the arrangements of the band of colors cast by the prism. What Hubble observes is a more than normal shift toward the red end of the spectrum, when the light from distant nebulae is analyzed in this fashion. The farther off the nebulae, the more marked the shift, hinting at the enormous velocities at which the bright clouds are flying out. Virtually the only proof of the expansion theory is this shift in the spectrum—toward the red end—which is always proportionate to the nebula's distance. This is known as the Doppler effect. The dimmer the star cloud or cluster, the redder is its spectrum, the faster the speed of its retreat from us, and our retreat from it. Instead of attraction, repulsion seems to be the dominant force in the cosmos. (Einstein had tried to show that the two forces, galactic attraction and repulsion, were more or less in balance, which helped to preserve a static universe.)

What conclusions follow from Hubble's upsetting theory? Eddington appraises the concept of the expanding universe and is led to a disturbing prediction: ultimately the galaxies will be so far apart from one another, that the cosmos will no longer be an entity. Another possibility is that Einstein is wrong in his premise that light travels faster than anything else. Either that, or else the universe must limit its ever accelerating expansion. But we, like Einstein, will not be on hand to find out the answer to that.

If the nebulae are rushing out from a cosmic center at an ascertainable rate of speed, astronomers should be able to compute just how long ago they started from that point— that is, fix a fairly exact date for the explosion of Lemaître's super-atom or Gamow's ylem. Some scientists are tempted by this idea, but the first to try it ran into this difficulty: the universe was apparently not as old as the earth. That cast doubt on Hubble's conclusions. The age of the earth can be fairly well estimated by geologists, who follow Lord Rutherford's principle and measure the radioactivity of rocks, how much uranium has been changed into lead in certain deposits—this ascribes a minimum age to the earth of about two billion years. But the figure obtained by Hubble's theory was only about one billion eight hundred million years, which means that the earth's formation preceded that of the surrounding cosmos, in which it is an infinitesimal speck. It is inconceivable that this should be so.

A group of Einsteinians had calculated that the universe, the stars, and the earth were all the same age, about two billion years. The creation of all three was a simultaneous event, or almost so. But cosmological figures are apt to change quickly! A later theorist, Omer, has recently declared that the universe is nearly half again as old as our planet earth, or about three billion six hundred million years. He reaches this guess by postulating that matter is not uniformly distributed. Indeed, says Omer, if nature had any such uniformity, the starry cosmos would be exceedingly unstable and act in a very erratic fashion. This is a highly radical concept, however, and again departs from Einstein. It also involves astronomers in mathematics so complex that no human mind can grasp them; and, if it is adopted, stargazers will probably have to resort to giant computing machines in order to determine or predict any celestial event.

By broader studies, meanwhile, a British geologist Arthur Holmes has corrected the data obtained from the radioactivity of rocks and decided that the earth's birth took place about three billion three hundred and fifty million years ago. Other scientists have supported this approximate figure by measuring (hypothetically) the increasing salinity of the oceans, and the presumable rate of recession of the moon. In view of this, the result gotten by Hubble's theory falls even further short, for now the earth would be twice as old as his universe.

From this serious dilemma, Hubble's "expanding cosmos" has been extricated in alternate ways: by resurrecting a part of Einstein's discarded physics (the "cosmological constant"—the effect of repulsive forces acting between galaxies over long distances) and giving it a new application; or else by accepting Behr's contention that most measurements of intergalactic distances are wrong; the galaxies are two times as far off as we supposed; hence they took twice as long to travel as far as they have, and the time when they started was that much earlier. Either way, Hubble is handily borne out.

More recently, the observatories at Mount Wilson and Palomar have reported findings which hint that though the galaxies *are* flying away, they do not always move at an increasing speed; at least, not at the constant rate of acceleration predicted for them as they get more distant. The sky-scanners do not bear out Hubble's "linear" speed-distance rule. Instead, when the galaxies are far out, they seem to decelerate. It has been suggested that measurements of such size must allow for an error of up to thirty percent, which is indeed a very large margin to tolerate. (But note, in the preceding paragraph, that Behr's measurements suggest recent errors up to one hundred percent.)

Meanwhile, too, Gamow has changed his estimate of the age of the universe—at least, from the time of the ylem's explosion—to five billion years, also a considerable upping of his previous calculation. This coincides with a figure arrived at by chemical tests of stone meteorites that reach us from outer space: how much helium they contain, and how much radioactive potassium 40 in relation to non-radioactive argon 40. Besides, what in the meteorites are the weights of various isotopes of lead? Electronic determinations of this have been carried out at Durham University and Oxford University by a pair of British professors, who believe they can learn the minimum age of the cosmos by this method. Tests on a meteorite that had traces of a rare gas, xenon 129, bore out this figure. The experiments were conducted by Dr. John H. Reynolds much later at the University of California.

Dr. E. J. Opik, of the Armagh Observatory, Northern Ireland, continues to place the age of the universe at about three and a half billion years, and as such twice the age he assigns to the earth. A few months after Opik's declaration, Professor A. C. B. Lovell of the University of Manchester announced his belief that the "primeval atom" disintegrated about twenty to sixty billion years ago. A considerable spread of time! (I believe that I have made my point, and do not wish to confuse the reader or try his patience too far. We are in the midst of controversy, where the age of the universe is concerned. I have consulted all the latest texts on this subject, and the figure most widely offered is ten billion years. Supporting this estimate is the subsequent sighting, by Dr. Rudolph Minkowski at Mount Palomar, of a galaxy at a distance of six billion light-years, three times farther out than any other heavenly object ever optically identified. If this finding is factual, it implies that the universe was in existence at the time the galaxy emitted its light, at least six billion years ago, and probably much earlier. A few months before Minkowski's report was issued, Dr. Allan Sandage, at the California Institute of Technology, suggested somewhat tentatively that his studies of the Milky Way placed its age at twenty-four billion years. He had arrived at this by a spectroscopic "analysis" of the chemical components of stars in the Cygnus group in that galaxy. If this is accurate, most other celestial yardsticks have been grossly in error. By studies of the isotopes of primordial osmium 186 and the later-formed osmium 187, Dr. Donald C. Clayton of the California Institute of Technology comes to a figure of ten to fifteen billion years for earth's heavy elements. He believes that he can calculate the original relative abundance of these two isotopes in the universe with some correctness; after which, he measures the radioactive decay of the more recent osmium 187 from rhenium 187, two heavy metals. This theory too is now being tested. All these estimates have been proclaimed in the public press within a space of less than three years.)

Other questions arise. What if the shift toward red on Hubble's spectrum (the Doppler effect) has quite a different significance from the one now read into it? Possibly the light which arrives at the earth from dim and distant nebulae is merely "tired"; possibly it has only lost some of its "energy"—the shorter waves which produce violet—in traveling so far and so has become longer and redder by the time it reaches our prisms. Some people think the solution is as simple as that. Then the nebulae might not be escaping at all, and the cosmos might not be blowing apart. At present, though, Hubble's "discovery" is accepted by nearly all the authorities in his field.

At the very least, as Behr suggests, the task of measuring distances to nebulae in such vast abysses of space offers many obstacles. The largest telescopes are adjusted to compensate for the rotation of the earth. But besides that, there are four other kinds of relative motion—if Hubble is right—to allow for in any measurement. One supposes that the minutest error could change our whole view of the cosmos. And there might be many other factors to account for, which are not now known. It is also possible—and consistent—that our whole superuniverse might be rotating about some other, or others, of equal or greater scope, of which we have had as yet no glimpse or sign. Who knows the true extent of the cosmos?

One hardly needs to restate here that very little in astrophysics can be checked by "facts." It is mostly in the realm of elaborate guesswork. For example, when light is analyzed in a prism—light from a nebula—no allowance is made for the age of the nebula, even assuming that it is known. The light ray has traveled millions or billions of light-years. It comes from a fiery object which was existing aeons ago. Astronomers assume that chemical compounds acted in the same way then, when the cosmos was that much younger, as they behave now. The assumption is logical and helpful but not provable. Nor do we know much about the influences that other parts of the universe might have exerted then or since on the object we are studying, which might have a major effect on the true state of it; yet certainly it does not exist in isolation in the cosmos.

Furthermore, as Professor Alastair Ward of Glasgow suggests, light beams might well collide with one another in space and thereby lose some of their energy; this too could cause a change in their wave length, and account for the Hubble-Humason red shift. But this is difficult to establish by experiment, and does not explain what happens to the lost energy, which raises another problem.

A California physicist, the late Richard Tolman, has

developed another aspect of Lemaître's theory, that two fundamental forces prevail in the universe, one of repulsion, which follows like a chain reaction from the original explosion, and one of attraction, which accounts for the accretion of matter in space. (This somewhat echoes Einstein's earlier postulate.) Tolman's view is that the universe will enlarge itself only until the outgoing, repulsive motion is balanced or offset by the inward motion or gravitational force. Then the universe must begin to contract or collapse upon itself, with accelerating velocity, until another single, heavy atom is formed at its center, which will grow too hot and finally explode to start the same process once again. Claude Stanush has cleverly compared this to the ancient Hindu belief that Brahma, the Creator, sits sublimely in the midst of the void, exhaling and inhaling the cosmos through his nostrils, forever. It is also in accord with a Jainist dogma that mankind grows larger and smaller in alternate cycles, from a height of less than one foot—when the race of man is at its worst—to one many times that.

Tolman's modification of Lemaître's guess also fails to answer the problem of what Gamow wittily describes as "St. Augustine's era." Gamow reminds us that it was St. Augustine of Hippo who first wondered "what God was doing before He made heaven and earth," or—as we might now put it—before He created the primordial cosmic atom.

Something like the Tolman theory of an oscillating universe has more recently been put forward by scientists at Princeton University and the Bell Telephone Laboratories at Holmdel, New Jersey, based on more recent observations of cosmic radio waves and light waves; and further support for this belief comes from Dr. Allan R. Sandage, gazing from Mt. Palomar, who hazards that the universe may be oscillating at the rate of one "bang" every eighty-two billion years! Dr. Sandage also announces the prevalence throughout the cosmos of a huge, and as yet uncounted, number of brilliant objects which he calls "blue galaxies," possibly forming galactic clusters.

III

But Abbé Lemaître made no positive claims for his theory. He presented it unassumingly in these words: "I believe that I have shown that the hypothesis of the primeval atom satisfies the rules of the game. It does not appeal to any force which is not already known. . . . But I shall certainly not pretend that it is yet proved, and I would be very happy if it has not appeared to you to be either absurd or unlikely." The Abbé has also strongly denied that his hypothesis was designed to fit any theological preconception.

Nonetheless, in 1951, the theory of the expanding universe, which has a beginning in time, received a token acceptance by the Church in a Papal Encyclical. Hubble's computations were also recognized by this statement and, by implication, approved. The Biblical account of the beginning is seen to be allegorical. Thus, in effect, the difference between science and religion is mediated. Pius XII declared, in substance, that Professor Hubble's observation that "galaxies tend to double the distance between themselves every thirteen hundred years" infers that "some ten billion years back in time these galaxies were all compressed in a relatively close space. This and the calculable age of the Earth's solid crust and the age of meteorites, and the oscillations of star systems add nothing to what the Christian learns in the first verse of *Genesis*. . . ." Says the Encyclical further: "Science has provided proof of the beginning of time, and the reasoning mind asks instinctively what preceded time?" The reply is a "creative omnipotence whose power . . . called to existence, through an act of love, matter and exuberant energy. Modern science bears witness to that primordial order of 'Let there be light' when nuclear particles broke forth from inert matter . . . and radiated forth, reuniting into galaxies."

With this, the Encyclical offers comment on St. Thomas Aquinas' first proof of God's existence, which is the omnipresence of change in all matter. (St. Thomas' argument: If there is not a God, Aristotle's "unmoved mover," who is the unchanging agency at the source, it would be necessary to imagine an endless series of "movers," themselves changing and being changed.) Pope Pius believed that modern science affirms this thirteenth-century Thomist logic, that of the proof based on the mutability of the cosmos. "By means of exact and detailed research . . . science has considerably broadened and deepened the empirical foundations on which this argument rests. . . . It has, besides, followed the course and direction of cosmic developments and . . . pointed to their beginning in time some five billion years ago. Thus, with that concreteness which is characteristic of physical proofs, it has confirmed the contingency of the universe and also the well-founded deduction as to the epoch when the cosmos came forth from the hands of the Creator." Concludes the Encyclical: "Hence, creation took place in time. Therefore, there is a creator; therefore, God exists. Although it is neither explicit nor complete, this is the reply we were awaiting from science."

But meanwhile, physics has come up with quite another theory which suggests that the cosmos is both beginningless and endless.

This hypothesis, "Continuous Creation," is the work of Bondi and Gold. It has been much popularized by Hoyle and recently endorsed by the British Astronomer Royal, Sir

Harold Spencer Jones. Some critics of Lemaître have objected that if the galaxies are moving out, the center of the universe is gradually being emptied, for a void is being left there. The heavy star clusters are in flight from the center. Bondi and Gold, both of whom were once at Cambridge University, contend that if the cosmos is expanding, and space is being "stretched," new space must steadily be added, and new matter is needed to fill it; otherwise the density of matter in space would be growing less and less. All this is in accordance with Einstein's "relativity." In the universe, between the galaxies and nebulae, there is interstellar gas, mostly composed of very thin hydrogen. The volume and weight of this interstellar material is far greater than that in all the stars and star clusters. If new matter is being added to our expanded cosmos, the chances are that it is also new hydrogen, the most common element, as well as the simplest and lightest. The galaxies retreat to what is for us the outer darkness, growing redder and finally disappearing from our sight. But meanwhile new ones are formed out of the fresh hydrogen (matter) in the space left open by the old ones. As long as this creative process goes on, the universe will never cease to be. Eddington's fear that future expansion will result in the cosmos seeming no longer an entity is invalid. The formation of new galaxies is endless. What causes the flight of the old galaxies? An original explosion? No, for there is no indication that any such explosion ever occurred. Instead, it is the very addition of the new hydrogen, the new matter, which causes the earlier galaxies to disperse; they are crowded or pushed out at an ever more rapid rate, just as a balloon expands when we add more air to it.

But where does the convenient new hydrogen come from? The ex-Cambridge men cannot guess; they do not even try to do so. Here is the mystical aspect of the theory. Sufficient, that it does appear. Something is being created out of nothing. Can sober scientists propose this? Hoyle defends his position by saying that the question of where the newly created matter arises from is senseless. "We do not ask, 'Where does gravitation come from?'; or if we do, science supplies no answer. Or again, we do not ask, 'Why do electric and magnetic forces occur in nature?' Instead we ask the questions: 'How does gravitation operate?'; 'How do electric and magnetic forces operate?' Science does not seek to justify the existence of gravitation or electromagnetism; what science does say is, 'If gravitation exists, then it works like this. . . .' or 'If electricity and magnetism exist, then they work like this. . . .' Exactly the same situation applies to the creation of matter. We cannot say why matter is created or where it comes from, but we can say, 'If matter is created continuously, then it is created in such and such a way. . . .' "

Speaking for this once-called Cambridge group, Thomas Gold (who is now at Cornell University) is quoted in support of Hoyle: "We must be on guard against that evil intruder 'common sense.' " He points out that common sense is derived from our daily experience with things of moderate size. But there exist objects far too large or far too minute to be observed by the naked eye or even by microscopes or telescopes. We cannot see subatomic particles, nor take in the distant galaxies. The laws that govern things perceptible to the human senses become such second nature for us that any departure from them seems wrong. Still, gravitation—one ruling common-sense force—is ignored by subatomic particles, which are attracted to one another by extremely strong forces effective at short distances only. To explain events in that "microphysical" world, scientists resort to the "unnatural" rules of quantum theory. In like fashion, the "megaphysical" world (larger than galaxies) apparently has its own laws. An example is the inexplicable force that causes the cosmos to expand, the galaxies fleeing from one another in place of being drawn together by gravitation. Gold propounds: "There may be many other such outlandish laws. It will not be easy to discover them, for scientists cannot play with huge, far-off galaxies as they do with neutrons and electrons."

Dr. Alastair Ward ingeniously postulates that the fresh hydrogen somehow (if as yet inexplicably) arises from the energy that is "lost" when photons in hurtling light rays cross one another's paths and collide in space. But he cannot quite suggest how this startling result comes about.

Bondi and Gold have computed the exact amount of new hydrogen required to keep their cosmos in perfect balance: one atom of it, to each quart of space, each billion years. Their cosmos has no center, for the creative process is going on everywhere simultaneously; and it has no limits. The receding galaxies go over an edge beyond perception; but the mass of newly formed hydrogen, from which the galaxies take shape, always equals the visible loss. The universe will expand forever.

A later refinement of this theory, put forward by Bondi and Professor Lyttleton (also of Cambridge University), speculates that the outward rush of the galaxies might be due to a difference in the electric charge of the proton and the electron in the hydrogen atom. The general assumption has been that the positive charge of the proton is exactly equal to the negative charge of the electron, and hence they stand off each other. But if the charge in the proton is larger by only one part in a million times a trillion—it is sometimes put as two parts in one billion billion—the whole universe would have to expand. "The galactic units must flee from one another. They were formed out of matter that was fleeing, and they must continue to flee." (This theory of a larger electric charge in the proton might also pinpoint the source of cosmic rays.) Unfortunately, no laboratory equipment as yet exists that can prove or disprove this daring notion, the measurements called for would be so infinitely small.

To this refinement, Gold and Hoyle have added still another interesting hypothesis: the "cosmological material" —i.e., the new hydrogen—is hot. This results from the break-up of its unstable neutrons, which releases so much energy that it reaches a temperature of one thousand million degrees K. The gas is spread so thin, however, that it does not affect nebular objects in the galaxies it surrounds. Nonetheless, the heat makes the intergalactic material expand like any hot, unconfined gas; and inasmuch as it fills the whole universe, the universe as a whole expands.

One thing which Bondi and Gold and the others of their group fail to do is to account for the origin of atomic species as effectively as Lemaître and Hubble with their cosmic egg, or Gamow and Alpher and Herman with their exploding ylem. But Hoyle believes that while the hydrogen atoms are perpetually formed from nothing, atoms of heavier elements are created later in the intensely hot interiors of unstable new stars (supernovae), and scattered everywhere by their occasional violent blow-ups. Some astrophysicists find this an unconvincing explanation. On the other hand, another Cambridge associate of Hoyle, cosmologist Dennis Sciama, argues that it is a far better one than the "primeval explosion" to answer the question of how the elements were distributed throughout the universe. He concedes that the heat of the original blast described by Lemaître might have caused a few elements to form, but not the heavier ones. Since there is no atomic nucleus of weight 5, the building-up process would have to stop at weight 4. The same difficulty would have occurred at weight 8. Indeed, the process would not have gone beyond helium. But explosions of supernovae occur not infrequently. Their temperature and density are roughly known and are high enough to make hydrogen atoms join together, forming all the heavier elements in about the right proportion.

It must be stated that so far no factual verification of "Continuous Creation" is possible. As with Lyttleton's startling idea about the unequal electric charges, the rate of process at which the new hydrogen appears is much too small to be registered on any instruments which we now possess, so it cannot be tested. It is hoped that a survey can soon be made with a Schmidt camera which will indicate something revelatory and relevant about the over-all density of matter in the universe. Bondi and Gold insist that this density is the same everywhere. We may soon know if they are right. The latest challenge to their theory is the reception of celestial radio signals that are thought to be caused by collisions between galaxies. These have been reported by Professor Martin Ryle at Jodrell Bank in England. In a cosmos of constant density, such collisions should be observed uniformly throughout space; but these appear to occur more frequently in the outer reaches amongst the oldest galaxies. The signals would emanate from events that took place billions of years ago, when the cosmos was far younger; they hint that space was denser then and encounters between galaxies more likely; hence the universe is evolving and changing. But Gold has sought to dismiss Ryle's findings as mere guesswork and probably erroneous.

The suggestion that the galaxies travel outward at an uneven rate—at first faster than Hubble believed, but then at a slower rate of acceleration—also contradicts the "steady-state" concept.

Explorer XI, which was sent aloft by the United States in April, 1961, to measure the intensity of paths of gamma rays, also seemed to controvert this theory, according to Dr. Robert Jastrow, a scientist then attached to the National Aeronautics and Space Administration. The level of gamma radiation was found to be so low, he reported, as to "rule out one version of the steady state of cosmology which holds that matter and antimatter are being created continuously." That is, the energy that should be left behind in the form of extremely strong gamma rays, if this theory is right, was not discerned by the gamma ray telescope that was placed inside the man-made satellite. Matter and antimatter would not collide and annihilate each other, without producing greatly heightened energy; but this was not detected.

Although "Continuous Creation" does not present us with a cosmos which has a definite beginning in time, and hence does not lend itself as well as Lemaître's concept to the buttressing of Thomism's first proof of God's existence, it is nonetheless a very optimistic theory, and one that religious people will like. Entropy, the second law of thermodynamics, decrees that the universe is running down; for when energy is uniformly distributed, it is no longer available for work. The inevitable end will be a stagnant cosmos, cold and dark. With that molecular uniformity, the universe will have come to rest: all life, light, and action will have been abstracted from it; even the galaxies will have dissipated their energy, and space will be filled with nothing but a vast dead stillness. Eddington, amongst others, prophesied this fate. But Bondi and Gold rescue the cosmos from such a prospect; for with the continuous appearance of new hydrogen, new energy is provided. God has not condemned the universe to extinction. A bright and active cosmos will go on forever.

16
STARS AND PLANETS

The Egyptians drew the world to resemble a bowl, ringed with high mountains. Egypt was at the very center. The sun journeyed across from rim to rim in a boat not unlike those which still traverse the Nile. In the dark sky, from a network of cables, hung the twinkling stars. Every four weeks, a hostile sow swallowed the moon piece by piece, after which it was reborn.

The Persians described earth as an island, shaped like a disk, in a shoreless ocean in which played the sportive Leviathan and other sea monsters. The firmament was a solid dome to which was affixed the zodiac.

The Hindus pictured a pyramidal heaven, mounted on a curved earth, which rested on the backs of four elephants, who in turn had their stance in the nether regions on a tortoise (a manifestation of Vishnu) that stood on a curled and hooded serpent, whose tail met his mouth in the upper world. But that was a metaphorical image for iconography, as were the Egyptian and Persian symbols. We need not suppose that an educated Egyptian actually thought the sun traveled in a praulike boat, or that an intelligent Hindu believed the cosmos to be encircled by a real serpent.

Most early races, however, seldom questioned that the earth was flat and the heavens a solid canopy. The visible stars were fixed to the sky, or else—like the sun and moon— were wandering and watchful gods. But were such pictures of the cosmos any more fantastic than ours? We have recently been told (by a confident lady astronomer at Harvard University) that the population of stars in the cosmos is in the *zillions!*

Such a vision is not wholly without mythological precedent, either. The Buddhist cosmos, magnificent in size and splendor, is one of millions upon millions of celestial universes—and no less than eighty-eight Buddhafields—radiant with the glow of their local deities, and stretching in ten directions of space from our little earth. This Oriental "space" is particularly one of unbounded distance and unimaginable circumference, for "infinity" has probably always been best conceived by the Eastern mind.

II

In our survey of scientific theories, we took up only those about the origin of the universe. A whole set of guesses about how the stars began are likewise available to us and should be included here. Astronomers say that most galaxies are spectacularly beautiful when seen through a telescope and have regular forms: spheres, ellipses, closed or open spirals. Such differences hint at an evolutionary sequence, but as yet there is no agreement on the order of it. One group of stargazers, typified by Jeans, claims that the spheres are young galaxies composed of cosmic dust and gas. With rotation, the dust and gas contract into stars, the galaxies flatten out in discs; the rotation increases, and they become spirals, ejecting matter by centrifugal force. But Harlow Shapley expresses an opposite view: the spherical galaxies are older, and the spirals are younger. He supports this thesis by observing that star clusters and star clouds are more evident in the spiral galaxies than in the spherical, and such clusters are signs of galactic immaturity rather than age. Short-lived supergiant stars are also more often glimpsed in the spirals; they signify instability, also indicative of galactic youth. Spherical galaxies show a more even distribution of stars, a stabler structure, and apparently are without the supergiants. All this is supposedly of interest to us, because it hints that our Milky Way is only in its first evolutionary stage, not its last. This gives our planet an extra lease on life, perhaps.

On the other hand, many astronomers—perhaps most—hold that all the galaxies are about the same age. The various types were shaped by their differing rotational speeds at the time of creation, and these speeds dictated how much of their primordial material coalesced into stars or went drifting freely in interstellar space in the form of thin clouds of gas.

A very interesting experiment that may relate to this debate—and also lend support to the theory of the exploding "primeval atom"—has recently been carried out in the physics laboratories of several American universities. Electrified atomic particles, carrying both negative and positive electrical charges, are shot out of a thimble-sized "atomic gun" of special design and subjected to a tremendous magnetic field. When this is done, photographs in the glass chamber reveal the emergence of tiny analogues of the stellar bodies, the "island universes": included are the many-armed spiral nebulae, which then progress through an evolutionary process in which they gradually lose their spiral arms until, in their final stages, they are ring-shaped. The pattern, here, is from the spiral to the spherical. This apparently simulates—on a subatomic scale—what on a cosmic scale would take enormous time. A billion years, in fact, is foreshortened in the laboratory to one half-millionth of a second. Infinitesimal copies of every variety of nebula beheld in the heavenly galaxies can be created in this way, again and again, under controlled conditions. Certain details of the experiment prompt speculation that what causes the galaxies to move apart—in an ever-expanding universe—is the conversion of gravitational energy into magnetic energy. As this transformed energy accumulates, it forms an ever-growing magnetic field around each galaxy which repels the magnetic fields around other galaxies also in early stages of development. But as yet no real proofs can be adduced from this experiment, which is on such a different scale from the cosmic; and, in any event, much in it is still left unexplained.

III

So far as we know, we see the Milky Way edgewise: our parent galaxy is an irregular spiral disk of stars, star clusters, dark cosmic dust clouds, and shining, ghostly nebulae, streaming out in lengthy filaments from an incandescent nucleus of stellar material. Other galaxies, too, have bright concentrations at their center, often so brilliant that they look like solid masses of light; but they also have the murky dust, the clouds of interstellar matter, which our new large telescopes and infrared photography have only begun to penetrate. Behind those clouds are almost always found more stars, demonstrating that most galaxies—our own amongst them—are much more populous than was formerly imagined.

With our new telescopes, the heavenly census goes on. As has been said, the instrument at Mount Palomar—at the moment our best—has a two-hundred-inch lens and explores a good portion of the seeable universe, a range of about two thousand million light years. The radius of the curvature of the explorable cosmos altogether is about ten thousand million light-years; beyond that, light rays will no longer carry to us, even though we use electronic "image-multipliers." If optical telescopes are mounted on earthborn satellites, an achievement which is presently projected, they might see more clearly because they will travel above our cloudy atmosphere; but they might not penetrate further, because they would have to be far smaller. But they might observe certain kinds of astral radiation (X-ray and ultraviolet) that are now denied to us, since earth's atmosphere shuts them out. Even radio astronomy has a limit already set, the time it takes signals from outer space to reach us, which in some instances would be too long for us ever to receive them. So, it would seem, an end will some day come to our ingenious questioning of the sky. Science will not go on searching forever, in that one respect.

Other galaxies reveal every sort of star which is numbered in our own Milky Way. By classifying them, astronomers hope to arrive at an evolutionary sequence for them, as well, and then decide how our sun originated and how it may end its career. Stars of different ages and masses and sizes and temperatures are presumably of different colors:

ruddy, steel-blue, white. To these must be added dark, dead stars which are detected but are usually invisible. Chemically, stars are largely hydrogen, but their energy is mostly the result of a nuclear reaction which changes the hydrogen into helium. Actually, this is only a guess; helium has never been produced from hydrogen in a laboratory, but temperatures in the hot interiors of stars would create new conditions there.

The ruddy stars, the exploding "red giants" or novae and supernovae, are the youngest. I have already mentioned them in an earlier chapter and described their dazzling flare-ups. Some devout astronomers like to think that the Star of Bethlehem was a supernova. Along with these "red giants" there are the variable stars, the Cepheids, which have periodic pulsations of luminosity. Shapley has established a valuable correlation between the brightness, length of pulsation, and distance of such stars. This, in turn, led Hubble to an important discovery about the Andromeda Nebula, which was later connected to his theory of the expanding universe.

The sky is also filled with dwarf stars, common but inconspicuous, and this category includes binary dwarfs which revolve around each other or one center in a close orbit. The novae are often such pairs or binaries, too. About half of all the visible stars are.

Photographs of our Milky Way suggest that stars of different spectral types and intrinsic brightnesses are mixed in it quite unevenly. They are a wide variety. But our galaxy and all the others appear to be very regularly distributed throughout the cosmos, at a distance from one another of about one hundred times their diameters. If this is true, it is a phenomenon of immense order. According to all the signs, there is a seeming progression in nature, from the small to the large and from the simple to the complex, which also applies to the astronomical realm:

atoms combine to form molecules, stars combine to form galaxies, and galaxies organize into clusters and super-clusters. All heed what we know of the laws of physics (unless Bondi's and Gold's theory of "Continuous Crea-tion" is truly well-founded). In addition to the five kinds of motion which were listed before, the galactic superclusters are unstable and go into inward and then outward oscil-lation. The outward movement is like that attributed by Hubble to the entire universe—the expansion—and con-tinues until all but a few of the central galaxies are scattered throughout the firmament, going off at last into the darkness we shall never pierce. Such outer regions may not actually be dark—they may be just as bright as our own portion of the universe; but not to us, since light from there will never get to us.

Recently, radio telescopes have "sighted" what seem to be five galaxies of extraordinary brightness. These puzzle astronomers. It has been postulated by Dr. Geoffrey Bur-bidge of Yerkes Observatory that these are "exploding galaxies," in which the blowing up of a supernova in a densely strewn stellar area has triggered a chain reaction of other supernova blow-ups, which accounts for the galaxy as a whole emitting highly intense radio waves. Another pos-sible explanation, put forward by Soviet physicist V. L. Ginzburg, is that these are protogalaxies, just taking form from their original gas clouds, and releasing gravitational energy and from that an unusual flow of cosmic rays in the process—this results in their radio-recorded "brilliance." These new phenomena are coming to be known as "quasars."

Hulst has declared that interstellar space is filled with exceedingly thin gas—lighter than any we know—and cosmic dust, tiny grains of matter. Such cosmic particles are about one-millionth of an inch in diameter and icy cold, only a few degrees above absolute zero. The interstellar gas consists of separate atoms or molecules; for them, heat is velocity and they are intensely hot. When the icy wandering grains of matter bounce against each other, they freeze and stick tight; when they collide with the hydrogen molecules of the interstellar gas, the molecules lose velocity and temperature. They also adhere to the particles, which grow larger, and the formation of a star is begun. The hot star thus originates, in part, by being very cold. The particles continue to grow at the cost of the separate atoms and the gas molecules surrounding them. Gradually they become large enough to exert gravitational attraction, which accelerates their rate of increase.

Even so, the universe is not old enough—by all present measures save the Bondi-Gold one—for the time required by this slow process described by Hulst. Spitzer and Whipple think that a more important factor than gravitation is the pressure of light from surrounding stars. This hastens the time of formation. The unequal radiation from near-by stars, especially in areas of mutual shadow casting, packs the larger particles into a thick, globular swarm. Bok and Reilly have disclosed the presence of such globules or protostars in our own Milky Way; they look like dark clouds, silhouetted against a brighter nebula. These are unborn stars; they are much larger than our sun, but probably weigh much less. As the thin clouds continue to concentrate, gravitation and the pressure of light act to whirl the dust in currents, and the particles get hotter and hotter. When in a billion years, perhaps, they are hot enough, a new giant shines in the sky, extremely bright. This is a contemporary process, too, and accounts for new stars in our own galaxy and elsewhere.

Once again, a puzzling question arises: if the cosmos is not as old as the aeons it would take a star to be formed in this way, without the added pressure of light, how was such pressure—"from surrounding stars"—exerted in the first place? Whence, in that initial period, came all the other stars which have been radiating light? The necessary conditions seem to be altogether too special: they are the kind most likely to be prevalent within huge intergalactic nebulae. The existence of a good part of the star population is still not explained. Spitzer and Whipple's theory does suggest, however, how stars might be formed now and in the future, in a universe already well-inhabited.

Struve believes that stellar rotation is also the result of the collision of streams of cosmic dust with the stars. Some stars whirl at almost ten thousand miles a second. At such a rate, they become unstable and shed rings of flaming gas. In a binary system, a portion of this ejected material may be captured by the companion, which thus increases its size. So, some stars are partially created of dust, and others are partially destroyed by it. What causes the stream of cosmic particles to flow toward the star is its gravitational pull, and there is also gravitational interaction between the two stars which have a binary relationship, if their orbit is really close.

Hoyle and Lyttleton (who, as we know, also collaborated with Bondi and Gold to produce the hypothesis of "Continuous Creation") have a theory rather like Struve's. The atoms of very rare hydrogen that uniformly fill space are drawn to one another. They become immense clouds, of incalculable weight, and they drift for billions of years, crowding into larger and larger gaseous masses which are the nascent galaxies. Time is hardly a factor for Hoyle and Lyttleton, since their cosmos is beginningless. The clouds swirl about in vast dark wheels—the darkness of the Hebrew *Genesis* still reigns—but as they contract and grow denser, they also grow hotter, with a transformation of gravitational energy into heat. In the center, ultimately, the hydrogen is changed into helium with an escape of energy which sets the whole reacting mass fearfully aglow. In some instances, the contraction stops at this point. If the energy generated at the flaming center is balanced by the radiation released at the surface, the star becomes stable for a long while. That would give a good picture of our sun, slowly "burning" its oxygen, and continuing for aeons. But there is another possibility, which determines the careers of some other suns. The stars, as they travel, pass through the remaining clouds of thin gas which occupy interstellar space. In doing so, they capture more and more cosmic particles from the gas swarms, which are also in motion. The number captured by this means would depend on the speed and density of the drifting clouds, but when too much interstellar material streams down and falls into the star, it may flare up, for its greater mass causes it to use up its hydrogen at an abnormally higher rate. The result is the supergiant which blows up with such spendthrift brilliance and burns itself out. When old stars "tunnel" through an unusually dense cloud, they may act like young ones, which possibly accounts for the exploding "blue giants," which brighten for a short-lived period much as the "red giants" do, then dim.

Recently, finer chemical analysis of several stars and star clusters has detected inexplicably wide deviations in their chemical constitution. One star, for example, contains one hundred times more phosphorus than our sun. Others vary vastly in the amount of lithium and beryllium they have. This raises a new question: Why do stars have such varied chemical natures if, as these theorists tell us, they were all created in more or less the same way? As yet, no reply has been vouchsafed.

IV

About the solar system with its planets more theories have been offered and more disagreements voiced than ever about the whole cosmos or distant stars. From the start, the ancients distinguished the brighter planets along with the sun and moon and noted their conspicuous wanderings and sought to explain them. Why did most stars appear to be fixed, while these few moved forever?

To the early Chaldeans, some six thousand years ago, the planets were the most fascinating phenomena of the heavens. From the Chaldeans' special interest in these "vagabonds" in the skyey belt called the zodiac, arose the fanciful pseudo science of astrology, which even today has its devout followers.

The Egyptians thought that the planets sailed their own smaller boats along canals that flowed from the Milky Way.

The famed Greek astronomer, Thales of Miletos, in the sixth century B.C., described the universe as a hemisphere afloat on an unlimited expanse of water: Earth was a flat disk similarly afloat within the hemisphere—a vision much like that popular amongst the Egyptians and Jews. He had studied in Egypt. He brought the principles of abstract geometry from there. He astonished his contemporaries by successfully predicting an eclipse of the sun, and measured the height of the pyramids by pacing off their shadows when his own shadow equalled his own height. What is more important, he rejected any intervention by the gods of Hesiod and instead offered a "rational" hypothesis to account for the origin of matter and the process of creation. Thales claimed that not "Eros"—Hesiod's nominee—was the "first principle" of all things, but water was. Other natural substances, for instance the air, only revealed their nature when water had evaporated from them. He was the first monist. (But he had not fully escaped from mythology; not only are there echoes of the "watery birth" in his cosmogony, but also, as said above, many influences of an Oriental lore that was still steeped in superstition.)

His pupil was Anaximander, who constructed a sundial at Sparta on which he illustrated the movement of, the planets, the obliquity of the ecliptic, and the sequence of the solstices, equinoxes, and four seasons. Possibly he was inspired to do this by ingenious Babylonian models he had seen. Anaximander also beheld the sky as "infinite" in extent and duration—it was not solid (no longer the shell of the "world-egg"); and even earth was not unique or unprecedented; a great host of other worlds had already had their being and had been dissolved. Earth was cylindrical in shape, suspended upright in air without support of any kind. It was enclosed in fiery spheres. Sun, stars, and planets were mere illusions: the sky might be compared to a huge flaming wheel; the sun was merely a hole in the rim of it through which a blaze escaped that was dazzlingly apparent to the naked eye. In the same way, the moon and stars were smaller apertures—even pinpricks—in the heavenly wheel.

Anaximander's "first principle" was not water but "a vast Indefinite-Infinite (*apeiron*), a boundless mass possessing no specific qualities, but developing, by its inherent forces, into all the varied realities of the universe. . . . From this characterless Infinite are born new worlds in endless succession, and to it in endless succession they return as they evolve and die. In the primordial Infinite all opposites are contained—hot and cold, moist and dry, liquid and solid and gas. . . ." (We remark here a strong resemblance to Taoism and the cosmic view of its founder Lao-tzu, who lived in the same era.)

Anaximenes, an associate of Anaximander, had a different opinion. Overhead revolved a transparent crystal sphere; the stars were attached to it. This simple belief was to have currency for many centuries. So too was Anaximenes' conviction that the "first principle" was air. (This motif, as we have seen, runs through much mythology.)

Xenophanes of Kolophon (also in the sixth century B.C.) beheld the cosmos filled with sun and stars that had no substance of their own; they were cloudy exhalations from earth that daily caught fire; by dusk or the next dawn, sun and stars had burned themselves out. New exhalations rose from the earth to replace them, the sun first and then the stars; and by noon or nightfall they flared up again. The moon too was a bright cloud of borrowed misty substance that was consumed every thirty days; then a new moon was fashioned. In different regions of the earth, men saw different suns and moons, none real objects, all phantasmal and cloud-born.

Lastly, in the same period, the powerful if ascetic genius of mathematics, Pythagoras of Samos, was persuaded that a celestial harmony existed in the arrangement of the planets, and that the true student of astral bodies might hear the music of those spheres. Said Diogenes: "Pythagoras was the first person to call the earth round, and to give the name of *kosmos* to the world." According to Pythagoras, the earth too revolved, like the wheel-affixed planets, to the east. It, like the sun and other heavenly travelers, moved about a central fire. The teachings of Pythagoras were greeted with religious awe. His influence was lasting, his errors and his truths intermingled; and consequently myth and "science" were to be indissolubly bound for over two thousand years.

In the fourth century B.C., Herakleides solved the problem of the irregular motion of the planets most happily: the two inner planets, Venus and Mercury, moved about the sun, and the others—the three outer ones—circled about the earth. Shortly afterward, Aristarchus daringly proclaimed the sun the center of the whole system but won few if any converts, though later Greek and Roman writers remembered his strange concept. So did Copernicus, who devoted a paragraph to Aristarchus; but later excised even the brief acknowledgment from his book!

By the second century A.D., in Alexandria, Claudius

Ptolemy's geocentric world—an immovable earth around which the sun and other planets wheeled in neat but intricate Platonic circles and epicycles—was fully conceived, and soon fixed on men's minds so firmly and for so long that it was to achieve the stature of a Christian dogma.

For thirteen hundred years, this "scientific truth"—Ptolemy's—was accepted with no question by the best minds of Europe, a fact which should give us pause. Only in the early sixteenth century did the timid Copernicus finally find courage enough to address his fateful and contrary tract to the Most Holy Lord, Pope Paul III: "In the middle of all sits Sun enthroned," he concluded his argument. "In this most beautiful temple could we place this luminary in any better position from which he can illuminate the whole at once? He is rightly called the Lamp, the Mind, the Ruler of the Universe; Hermes Trismegistus names him the Visible God, Sophocles' Electra called him the All-seeing. So the Sun sits as upon a royal throne ruling his children the planets which circle around him. The Earth has the Moon at her service. As Aristotle says, in his *de Animalibus,* the Moon has the closest relationship with the Earth. Meanwhile the Earth conceives by the Sun, and becomes pregnant with an annual rebirth." (We observe how, even in this revolutionary treatise, poetry and mythology infuse fact.)

Some decades later, the myopic Johannes Kepler was still listening for Pythagoras' harmonious "music of the spheres." While brilliantly plotting the accurate orbits of the planets, Kepler obstinately held to credence in astrology, too. "That the sky does something to man is obvious enough; but what it does specifically remains hidden," he complains. Kepler's belief is shared by his master, Tycho Brahe—the Danish astronomer with the gold-and-silver nose—who startled his fellow men by his precise observations of the stars but at the same time delved into arcane rites of alchemy. These were "men of science"—indeed, amongst the greatest in all history—but not yet free of illusions.

V

In our "modern" era, significant speculation about the *origin* of the planets started in the eighteenth century. Emanuel Swedenborg, another mystical physicist, anticipated the thinking of French naturalist Georges de Buffon, whose idea it was that the planets had been born in consequence of a collision between our sun and a passing comet.

A theory which does not presuppose an accidental encounter was next introduced by Immanuel Kant. As we shall see, Kant's ingenious guess has never entirely lost scientific favor. He postulated that the planets and the sun were formed from a single, large rotating gaseous cloud which gradually condensed. Some forty years later, Pierre de Laplace modified Kant's theory. He agreed, however, that a nebula was the source—a flat, rotating cloud of diffuse gas—which shrank as it cooled and in the process spun faster and faster, at intervals flinging off gas rings. Each ring coalesced into a planet. His model, plausibly chosen, was Saturn and its rings.

Laplace's hypothesis was accepted for over a century. I have already mentioned that it was the one which I was taught in high school. But long before the theory was transmitted to me, in my early teens, the English physicist Clerk Maxwell had shown it to be based on false physical premises. Or so, at least, it was presumed in Maxwell's day, when less was known than now. Though the rings might not coalesce for the reasons or in the way Laplace proposed, they might—in the latest light of science—do something like it for other causes. Even so, the Kant-Laplace hypothesis failed to explain the greater angular momentum of the outer planets, which is one of the ticklish problems to be faced.

My high school teacher, an elderly, dear man, was about a generation behind the times. Or rather, he was teaching me what he himself had learned in his youth, as teachers usually do. Just after the First World War, the Chamberlin-Moulton theory became popular; and it was this, as I have said, I studied in my college astronomy course. It never occurred to anyone in our class, except the young Fundamentalist, to doubt its validity. Certainly it was offered by our college professor as gospel. As imagined by Chamberlin and Moulton, a wandering star entered our part of the heavens and pulled out of the sun the stuff—jets of matter—which later collected in large masses. These continued to revolve about the sun. The planets were originally smaller than they are now. They resembled the asteroids, fragments of matter that also orbit around the sun, and grew by accretion. Hence, this is best known as the "planetesimal hypothesis."

Sir James Jeans, the noted English astronomer, had developed a very similar hypothesis at almost the same time. He described how the passing star lifted a huge tide on the flaming surface of the sun. Eventually, a long filament of sun material was detached by this near collision or grazing and broke up into major segments. This picture is heightened by Professor Harold Jeffreys: the sun and star struck fully and then veered apart, leaving behind them a trail of their mingled substance; the planets were shaped from this.

Such spectacular theories have now been discredited by Spitzer and Russell. The only result of our sun and an invading star coming too close, if it had ever happened, would have been an immense explosion. The temperature of any matter expelled by the sun in such a near collision or rape would be so high that it would expand and dissipate into a formless cloud. The heat would be about one million degrees centigrade, and no planet could be born in that. The expansion would go on more than one hundred times as fast as the heat loss, so there would be no chance for the ejected sun material to cool in open space. This applies to still another hypothesis, put forth by Lyttleton, which is that the sun was once a double star, and that a third star crashed into the sun's companion carrying part of it away; and the planets were built from its debris.

Von Weizsäcker has yet a different guess. In the beginning, the sun was surrounded by a huge cloud of very thin gas in which were vortices of laminar flow; and, in these, whirls were formed in which the cosmic dust bounced against other dust. What is involved here is the exceedingly complex dynamics of "turbulent motion." Richardson has written a poem (quoted by Gamow, in another instance) which serves us rather aptly:

> Big whirls have little whirls
> That feed on their velocity;
> And little whirls have lesser whirls,
> And so on to viscosity.

Or, it might be said, the planets are evolved by the aggregation of fine cosmic dust, in regions of contact, over a period of about one hundred million years. If this explanation is true, then the same process must have taken place in the shaping of practically all the stars in the cosmos, and they too have planetary systems. This inspires Gamow, a supporter of von Weizsäcker, to conclude that those other planets are most likely inhabited by life in its highest stage of development.

Besides his theory about the formation of stars by the

pressure of light, Dr. F. L. Whipple has a guess, too, about the origin of the solar system. He thinks that the sun and its planets were born simultaneously, from the same cloud of natal cosmic dust. It was about five trillion miles across. While this whirling cloud was contracting, affected by the minute pressure of starlight, the "turbulent motion" of the dust particles became so accelerated that shock waves were set up. The cloud suddenly collapsed, fell in upon itself, to form a nuclear, incandescent mass at its center of gravity: our sun. The outer and dominant stream of lesser dust aggregates, the embryo planets, was still spiraling in when this occurred and the collapse stranded it in space. Whipple's theory is very simple and answers many questions which others do not. Friction heated the sun and the planets, but only the sun—which has so much more mass—remains fiery at the surface. Our moon could have been detached in much the same fashion, when the earth itself condensed. Some planetary orbits crossed and collisions took place. One lost or ghost planet, which originally followed an ellipse between Mars and Jupiter, was broken up by such a crash, leaving only fragments which still travel on its former path. That explains the orbit of the asteroids, which have the same chemical composition as our earth. Some of them are three hundred miles in diameter. Like Weizsäcker, Whipple holds the opinion that there are many embryonic planets in the far-off dark nebulae, which have still to develop into young galaxies. The unborn planets are still in the wombs of unborn stars; and doubtless there are fully grown ones in the older galaxies. Contracting clouds of dust and gas may have filled them all with millions of circling planets. It is more logical to believe that, than to think the creation of the solar system was an exceptional happening, or that we are unique.

Some weight is added to this belief by Strand's proof,

arrived at mathematically, of a dark companion circling around one of the stars in Cygnus, The Swan. Sixteen times as large as Jupiter, this dark body travels about its parent star a little less than once in five years. So far no one has seen Strand's planet, the name by which it is known, and it is hardly likely that anyone ever will: it is too far, too small, and too dark. But its mass, probable chemical composition, diameter, and surface temperature have already been computed. It may or may not be habitable. Professor Henry Norris Russell of Princeton University has concluded from this mathematical evidence that there are countless more like it, and that probably thousands of them in the Milky Way galaxy alone are able to support life. This is impressive testimony, since Professor Russell is often spoken of as the greatest living astronomer. On the other hand, a suspicion arises in some minds that if Strand has made the slightest error—which is possible, even though it is most unlikely—he could populate the whole universe with unseen planets that really have no existence. Or what if the dark companion is not a planet but a burnt-out star? At that distance, an astronomer, measuring the "oscillations" of a binary system and deducing from them the presence of a third body, might unavoidably make a mistake.

But another scientist, Professor D. ter Haar, finds Whipple's hypothesis inadequate. It does explain some of the unusual characteristics of the solar system—the differences in the angular momentum of the planets, for instance—but leaves many others untouched. So Ter Haar advances a theory of his own. He revives Kant's vision but changes it to a degree. The sun was first surrounded by a large cloud of gas, the center of which was shaped into a flattish disk by its revolution. The increasing density of the center decelerated its rotation there, while the peripheral section whirled faster. That is why the outmost planets—Jupiter, Saturn,

Uranus, Neptune, Pluto—have most of the angular momentum, or "energy of rotation." The inner planets—Mercury, Venus, Earth, Mars—are smaller and denser. Ter Haar says that the sun's cloud was hotter toward its center and cooler toward the edge. This range in temperature resulted in the formation of various kinds of solids, as the gas condensed. Only heavy substances of high boiling points—metals and mineral compounds, silicates—could coalesce in the fiery inner region. Only in the cool periphery could light compounds such as ammonia and methane, water or ice, hydrocarbons gather in masses. The outer "protoplanets" were constructed from more of the compounds and grew more rapidly. Similarly, their size helped them to draw to them quickly almost all the gas left in the sun's atmosphere; the inner ones, growing more slowly, had less gravitational pull. The consequence: the outer planets are big and "soft," while the inner four are comparatively small and dense. (We have seen, of course, that the number of planets has grown from five in the time of the Greeks, to nine today.)

An even more recent neo-Kantian hypothesis is that of Professor Gerard P. Kuiper. He also takes his point of departure from Ter Haar. His special field is hydrodynamics, and particularly vortical motion. Kuiper offers us this series of images: one third of the sun's swirling cloud contracted to a thin pancake ring around it, like those encircling Saturn. The thickness of this ring was only one percent of its diameter, and it revolved in the plane of today's orbits of the planets. Its density was not uniform, but was thinner further out. When its density reached a critical point, it broke up into several whirling eddies, the "protoplanets." This continued to shrink and at last condensed into the planets, with rings of loose material around them, which ultimately became their satellites. An exception is Saturn, where the disks are narrower and too near the planet, so that they failed to combine into moons. The earth's moon, however, is not a normal satellite like the others, but was instead a double planet, with earth as its partner and formed simultaneously. All this occurred about three billion years ago. The critical density for the condensation was not equal throughout the primordial pancake ring. It was one million times higher near Mercury than near Neptune, for example. Solar tides, influencing the eddies or "proto-planets," explain why the planets rotate in the same direction. The whole shaping of the solar system took only a few thousand years, and of the satellites barely a century. Kuiper also believes that the sun's family is not a unique phenomenon. Many other stars, in other galaxies, could have similar systems.

Hoyle, one of the sponsors of "Continuous Creation," hypothesizes along very different lines from Ter Haar and Kuiper. He goes back to Lyttleton's suggestion that the sun was originally a binary—but Hoyle proposes that its companion, a "red giant" or supernova, blew up. Such explosions are caused by the star's inner production of gaseous heavier elements. Though most of the debris of the companion did escape from the sun's gravitational field, a share was captured. The hot gas thus caught by the sun became a revolving ring around it, and the heavier elements in the ring clotted and condensed into planets and satellites. Hence, the planets are composed largely of those heavy elements, not of hydrogen and helium like our central star; and hence they revolve rapidly at a distance from the slowly turning sun, of which they were never really a part. The planets are not children of the sun, but are changelings; they have been rescued or kidnapped. Since supernovae blow up every two or three hundred years in our Milky Way, as well as in the other galaxies, and many of the flaring stars are binaries, Hoyle is quite certain that other planetary systems have being elsewhere. He calculates that since the beginning of the Milky Way ten million giant stars have blown up and become dim dwarfs, in a period of almost four billion years. Not less than one hundred thousand of them have left behind them systems—forever invisible to us—in which one planet, at least, possesses the temperature and chemical content favorable for fostering life. Probably, Hoyle propounds, life has developed in the same way on those other one hundred thousand distant worlds as on earth. They may even have superior races akin to the human one. Some would think this fanciful romancing, but it is issued under the aegis of Cambridge University.

A Swedish astrophysicist, Dr. Hannes Alfvén of the Royal Institute of Technology in Stockholm, puts forth yet another possible explanation. He dismisses such theories as Ter Haar's, because they are based on hydrodynamic principles, which Alfvén asserts apply only in special regions, such as earth's ocean and the lower strata of our atmosphere. Most of the universe, however, including the stars and interstellar space, is comprised of ionized gases whose atoms are affected by heat or radiation. To understand their behavior, one must be acquainted with magnetohydrodynamics, instead. This is a new phase of science of which Dr. Alfvén himself is a founder. He supports his theory by experiments with a "homopolar" device that has been used in laboratories to study what happens to hot or electrified gases in conditions such as Dr. Alfvén has hypothesized.

The solar system, he thinks, grew out of a nebulous cloud, between one and one-tenth of a light-year wide, rotating slowly within our galaxy. When the sun initially took form within the hot, humid ionized cloud, with increasing rotation, its powerful magnetic field repulsed the peripheral, electrically charged segments of the cloud. But as the cloud gradually cooled, some of its ionized atoms joined with electrons, until the atoms became electrically neutral, which allowed them to fall inward toward the sun. After they had traveled in a few hundred million miles, drawn by gravitation and gaining immense speed, they hit against the thin gas enveloping the sun, and were ionized once more by the energy of collision, until the sun's magnetic field stopped them short. Easily ionized chemical elements were arrested well away from the sun; some that were harder to ionize got much nearer to the sun before they were halted. Dr. Alfvén says that his laboratory experiments show that gases or particles rotating in an electric field do form such bands as these.

One segment of cloud, composed chiefly of hard-to-ionize elements, stopped about sixty-seven million miles out from the sun, near the present orbit of Venus. With its cooling, part of its material condensed into dust. The dust grains grew steadily bigger by attracting each other, and ultimately coalesced to form Mercury, Venus, Earth. In the same manner, another segment of the cosmic cloud, halted still further from the sun, became Mars and the moon. Since these two regions of planet formation overlapped, the earth chanced to capture the moon, now its satellite. The big outer planets, Jupiter, Saturn, Uranus, and Neptune, took shape in a third portion of the cosmic cloud, its chemical composition having caused it to be ionized and held at a very great distance from the sun. (Too little is known as yet about the ninth planet, Pluto, for it to come under discussion here.) Alfvén believes that this theory gives nearly every star a "retinue of planets."

One possible flaw in detail in Alfvén's explanation is Dr. Harold C. Urey's recent heretical claim that the moon is actually very much older than the earth. He thinks it might even have predated earth by a hundred million years. (Dr. Urey has won the Nobel Prize for chemistry.) He refers to the moon as one of the few remains of an early phase of the solar system. His hypothesis gains particular credit because it accounts for the strange lightness of the moon, which is only three-fifths as dense as the earth. As Dr. Urey pictures it, the sun was ignited by a gravitational pile-up of dust which finally became massive enough to press out or expel the thermonuclear reactions in its core. Around this "hydrogen bomb furnace" was a circular cloud within which there took shape numerous moon-sized bodies. These thronging moons frequently crashed against one another, littering the solar system with their debris. The outward pressure of the sun's light, gas, and magnetic force dispersed and swept out much of the lighter material, before the rest fell together again and consolidated as the planets.

Dr. Urey says that the moon, due to its weak gravity, cannot hold on to gases, but apart from that its mixture of elements is much like that of its parent sun. But the earth, being a "second-generation" body, possesses far more iron and other heavy materials. (Dr. Gold, on the other hand, has sought to explain the lighter weight of the moon by suggesting merely that, beneath its top strata, there is much ice and water.)

Meanwhile, a few months earlier, Professor M. M. Woolfson of the University of Manchester published still another consideration of how the solar system has come about. This theory really hails back to Sir James Jeans's earlier hypothesis that a star, passing close to the sun, tore out chunks of matter that coalesced into the nine major satellites.

The mysterious regularity in the distances of the planets from the sun is a fact first established in 1772. It is known as the Bode-Titius Law. Professor Woolfson cites his calculations on the University of Manchester computer to show that the near passage of a star would indeed cause the planets to take up positions in accordance with this two-century-old law. The star, setting up tides on the sun, would pull solar material away at fixed intervals of six and three-quarter years, with Venus being formed first, and then the other planets in due succession. Mercury alone does not occupy its proper place in the heavens by these new computations, but Professor Woolfson posits that Mercury, the innermost planet, did not begin its present track about the sun at the same time as the other eight planets. Instead of a single destroyed planet between Mars and Jupiter—the asteroid belt—two planets might have been formed there six and three-quarters years apart; and these, colliding, may have been the source of the fragments that comprise the scattered asteroids still traveling in that orbit.

From all that has been quoted here, we can see that there is no end to the making of theories about the origin of the solar system. We may wonder at which point in history these hypotheses should be regarded as soundly "scientific"—many of them obviously are not—rather than still mythical. They are the daydreams of astrophysicists. Above all, we note that a good many of these stories sound like yet another kind of dismemberment myth. Out of the womb of the cosmic dust cloud—Tiāmat—the stars and the planets are created. Out of the body of the hacked giant—the supernova, or is it Ymir?—the firmament comes into being. Man has not changed his mode of thinking. The mathematician, in his Cambridge laboratory, seems to have the same ineluctable thought processes as the ancient mythmaker. It is almost as though he cannot think in any other fashion, no matter how much he conceals it from himself and others with new language and new symbols. The story of creation is obstinately always the same.

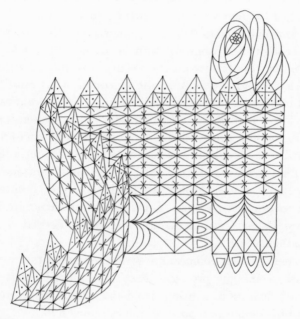

17

LIFE AND EVOLUTION

Guesses about the origin of man began with scientists long before Charles Darwin. Plato offered one, to fit a design that was mathematical. God had created a spherical cosmos. He had also enclosed the "divine causes" in a sphere, or what we now term the head, when He formed man. The head required help, otherwise it might roll or tumble along the deep or high places of the earth. Consequently, the body was added to it, and the body had length and was provided with four limbs extended and jointed.

Mathematicians, indeed, are always eager to apply their calculations to the natural sciences. They are seldom discouraged by their sometimes startling results. Bishop Usher, an Irish divine famous in the Renaissance, used his pencil late at night and came up with an exact figure: man was created by the Trinity on the twenty-third day of October, 4004 B.C., at nine o'clock in the morning. What must have most impressive to his sixteenth-century contemporaries was the "nine o'clock in the morning," the authenticating detail, the one which sounds most precise and scientific. It is hard to believe that anyone could simply invent a figure like that. We have already seen, in the similar instances of Lemaître, Gamow, Alpher, and Herman, that nothing is more overpowering than a mathematical demonstration. Bishop Usher, in consequence, was much heeded by the unmathematical.

Fernel, another Renaissance savant, observed that a dead carcass seemingly produces bees and other insects and reached definite conclusions from that about the source of life which he put in a popular and esteemed book.

But how recent is the Theory of Evolution, which today dominates so much of our thought? Because we consider it modern, we are apt to respect it that much more, but actually it is not. Thales, the first Greek philosopher, held that all things came from water. We have also noted that Anaximander, his pupil, applied this idea to living creatures and even to mankind. "Fish or fishlike beings were born of warm water and earth. In these beings men were formed. Men and women came out, already capable of sustaining themselves." Kerényi quotes from a Greek compilation and tells us that Anaximander's beings which arose "in the damp" were plantlike as well as fishlike, and were initially wrapped and protected by a sheath of acanthus leaves. But elsewhere Anaximander is made to say that external heat dried some of the fluid world into land and evaporated some of it into clouds, while the variations of heat overhead caused the motions of the winds. By gradual stages living organisms arose in the world-sea; land animals were originally fishes, and only with the drying of the shores did they acquire their present shape. "Man too was once a fish; he could not at his earliest appearance have been born as now, for he would have been too helpless to secure his food, and would have been destroyed."

Xenophanes, too, taught that all things, including mankind, had a sea origin; the waters had once covered nearly all the earth, as was evidenced by the discovery of marine fossils far inland and even on mountaintops.

Aristotle anticipates Darwin and writes: "Nature proceeds little by little from things lifeless to animal life in such a way that it is impossible to determine the exact line of demarcation." He deemed the ape an intermediate form between man and other reproductive creatures.

More directly, Buffon and Hume foreshadowed the evolutionary theory; as did Darwin's own grandfather, from whom the grandson borrowed so much with no public acknowledgment. Indeed, if Barzun is right, there are signs that the ungenerous Darwin tried to conceal his dead grandfather's contribution, wishing all the credit himself. Linnaeus classed man among the higher primates. Diderot, Bonnet, Maupertius were all forerunners in some details, which makes part of the theory a century older. Largely, it belongs to the mid-eighteenth century, not the late nineteenth. Lamarck said that the giraffe had stretched his neck while seeking high foilage. Besides that, Lamarck spoke of "new needs" and "disuse" to explain the presence of rudimentary organs.

A Romantic natural philosopher and scientist, Oken of

Jena, in Germany, also held this view in the very early nineteenth century (I quote here from Kerényi once more): "The first man must have developed in a uterus much larger than the human one. This uterus is the sea. That all living things have come from the sea is a truth nobody will dispute who has occupied himself with natural history and philosophy. Contemporary science disregards every other doctrine. The sea has nourishment for the foetus; slime to be absorbed through its membranes, oxygen for these membranes to breathe; the foetus is not confined, so that it can move its membranes at will even though it should remain swimming about for more than two years. Such foetuses arise in the sea by the thousands if they arise at all. Some are cast up immature on the shore and perish; others are crushed against rocks, others devoured by carnivorous fishes. What does that matter? There are still thousands left to be washed, soft and mature, on to the beaches, where they tear off their membranes, scratch for worms, and pull mussels and snails out of their shells." And Oken goes on to discuss the evolution of animals from plant life. "The animal, not merely poetically speaking but in actual fact, is the final flowering or true fruit of the plant, a genius rocked on the flower." Kerényi says that not only is Oken's scientific thinking inadvertently mythological—the parallel story of the sea birth of Maui, the Polynesian, reveals as much—but the Jena philosopher was also acquainted with the image of Prajāpati, very likely through the mythological studies of the Romantics. Compare this last passage in Oken, invites Kerényi, to the noted one in the *Upanishad* tale: "This world was water, a single flood; only Prajāpati could be seen, sitting on a lotus-leaf." Not only is the essential concept the same as in the Hindu creation myth, but Oken unawares resuscitates Harpocrates, too, the Egyptian sun child, who is also frequently shown resting on a lotus blos-

som, as though he were its greatest flower. Kerényi concludes from this that the primordial images were not merely
revived in early nineteenth-century science such as Oken's;
instead, they had always gone on living, from Anaximander
to Darwin. They come to us from very primitive man, many
of whose totem ancestors were plants: trees, nuts, fruits.

Perhaps Kerényi could have made his point with a wealth
of clearer examples, because they do abound.

II

The Arunta of Central Australia relate how the Ungambikula, the Self-existent Spirits, came down from the sky
with long stone knives. They caught embryonic forms of
life which swam in the salt water, in the sea shallows of the
shore, and with the knives shaped them into complete
human forms. This embryonic life included the ancestors of
the large lizard, the Alexander parakeet, and the small rat,
and grass seed and the plum tree, which became the totems
of the Arunta. Finally, the Ungambikula circumcised the
new people—all except the Plum Tree Man—and themselves turned into tiny lizards.

We have already heard similar stories of man's lizard
origin told by the Dieri of Western Australia, and the Fan
of Africa; and we have learned that the Tibetans boasted
of their descent from monkeys, as do the Dafia tribesmen of
northeast India. What is evolution, indeed, but another
form of totemistic myth? Sir James Frazer ventured to say as
much, in a brief essay, at the time when the controversy
between Darwinism and Fundamentalism was at its loudest.
But Frazer's essay was little read. One reason for the evolutionary theory's popular acceptance, though, could be
that it falls in with an ancient human habit of thought.
The belief that man has animal ancestors is hardly recent:
it belongs to early humanity.

Empedocles, a philosophical mystic who lived and preached five hundred years B.C., propounded that lumps of earth and water, cast up by Sicilian volcanoes, developed into men with the heads of bulls, and bulls with the heads of men. This process continued, until these hybrid forms of life were gradually eliminated and the various species of animals and men known to us today were evolved. In some respects, this accords with Darwin's theory, and in other details even goes beyond it to agree with more modern hypotheses. For instance, a Mexican scientist, the biologist Herrera, thinks that life might have come from lava. At least, on the scale of bacteria. He has mixed chemicals from volcanic emanations—formaldehyde, ammonia, sulphur, and cyanogen—and obtained from them about six thousand different microscopic forms, all of which display some of the properties of microorganisms. Herrera does not assert that these test-tube things are truly alive, but they act remarkably like amoeba, spores, and chromosomes, which fix heredity. In fact, they imitate the whole microscopic world, and in chemical analysis they produce certain reactions. Sulphur, cyanogen, and ammonia could be the basis of continual synthesis, or creation, of life from inorganic matter. It has already been shown in the laboratory that microscopic things can be crystallized which, though presumably not alive, behave much like living cells. The early world, Herrera suggests, was most likely molten and volcanic.

The latest picture offered by science, however, has the appearance of life predating the earliest volcanic activity or lava flow. This is the guess of Harold C. Urey, but it is self-confessedly only another example of professorial fantasy. It is one of many highly dramatic accounts of the planet's dawn. Light stony silicates were the first substances precipitated from the primeval dust cloud, and became the cores of the earth and its moon. (Urey offered this "history" before he submitted his theory that the moon is actually far older than the earth.) Much later, heavy iron followed. The earth was not yet solid, but fairly cool and unstable, with a center of light rock around which was a thick layer of relatively heavy stone mixed with iron. Over this was another very thin stratum of stone. The entire surface was covered with ocean, in whose depths life began a billion and a half years ago or earlier. These ancient creatures have left no trace, because all were pelagic, swimming at or near the top of the sea. They deposited no heavy shells or skeletons as fossil remains; they did not develop any, since there were still no shores or shallows for nonfloating things to live on.

Meanwhile, the radioactive elements in the earth were heating up its hitherto cool mass. The iron melted and collected at the core, with the lighter materials rising toward the surface. The molten land pushed above the waters at last; the seas were shunted to one side and rimmed, very much as on the third day of division in the Hebrew *Genesis,* when the oceans and mountains were gathered in their separate places.

Probably earth was one large continent at first, Urey speculates, but as the hot core material went on rising and spread out in lava flows near the surface it broke into sizeable segments which were carried apart by the same upward thrust. This accords with Wegener's theory of continental drift, that the eastern coasts of North and South America look as though they had been split away from Europe and Africa. On a map, this is very apparent. But recently some rare gorceixite pebbles were picked up south of Dakar, in Sierre Leone, and along the Gold Coast, in Africa. Before now, gorceixite was a mineral found only in Brazil, whose bulge could very neatly be fitted into the indented shores of Sierre Leone and the Gold Coast. The continental drift, if factual, helps to explain why the earth's axis is tilted at its present angle, too. The gravitational pull of the sun and the moon, and the centrifugal force of the earth's rotation, might also have been responsible for the break up of the original land mass. Some geologists insist that the great continents are still drifting. Greenland and Scotland are thus sixty feet further apart every year, although the people of those two places seem not to notice it and go about their daily affairs as usual.

Wherever life first emanated, from fiery lava or from the salt sea, we have only an inkling of its original nature. No fossils, except of algae, are left from the Pre-Cambrian era, to which life almost certainly goes back. The odds are for a water birth, as in the many myths in that category, because chemically life and water are practically synonymous. Today there are no known organic compounds in the sea which are life-producing; and, if there were, living organisms would destroy them at once. But in earlier days, such molecules might have had being indefinitely, and contact between two of them might have led them to join and become a larger whole; and so on, until the ever more sizeable and more complicated molecule could grow by absorbing others. Finally, it might attain the ability to reproduce itself. Garrison has dissolved a little ferrous sulphate and carbon dioxide in pure water, contained in an ingeniously designed glass cell, and shot through it a high-energy helium ion beam from a cyclotron. When this is done, a little of the carbon dioxide combines with water and yields formic acid and formaldehyde. Solutions of the formaldehyde can change into sugar. Ocean water might once have held carbon dioxide and other organic chemicals. High-energy radiation from cosmic rays or lightning discharges might have impregnated this virgin solution as it does for Garrison and other experimenters (and exactly as in the Zuñi myth of the Sun Father, who creates the world by impregnating a foam cap with a light ray). It seems quite likely that this radiation, or a volcanic heating of the waters, brought forth the necessary formaldehyde. Next, in a billion years or more, this simple stuff may have been transformed into sugars, proteins, and ultimately into vital particles. Much work along these lines, still inconclusive, has been done at the Oceanographic Institute in Florida and by Dr. Gerhard Schramm at the Max Planck Institut in Tübingen, Germany; and by Ceylonese biochemist Cyril Ponnamperuma at Lawrence Radiation Laboratory in California.

One school of scientists, however, likes to think that life, in the form of such minute organisms, really came here from other planets or stars. To do so, the tiny travelers would have to survive cosmic rays, and absolute cold, and intense heat, but various theories are brought forward to show that even this is possible. Becquerel's experiments have proved that simple and quiescent forms of life can endure the most extreme ranges of temperature. Some mustard and wheat seeds were exposed to two hundred and fifty degrees centigrade below zero, which is the temperature of liquid hydrogen, and still germinated. Even if the sun were to be extinguished and our atmosphere to vanish, there might be a lingering for a long time on our frozen planet of seeds and germs, spores of organisms, if Becquerel is right. It is even possible that under the thawing influence of radiations from a new source in the universe, not a few frozen flows of protoplasm might be reborn and stream again. So the temperature of interstellar space is not a certain obstacle to the transfer of life from one star to another.

The next question is how would even bacteria overcome

gravitation. The pressure of light might be of aid. Lebye-deff has deflected the falling spores of a plant from their gravitational course by passing them through an extremely strong beam of light in a glass test tube. In this way, bacilli might escape the earth and journey to Mars in twenty days or to Jupiter in eighty days, at the speed of light. The sun pushes them, against the gravitational grasp of the earth. The minute organisms might have come and still be coming from other celestial bodies in that fashion, or be riding here on meteors. But that merely shifts the problem: how did life originate on the other planet or star?

The most considerable threat to such spores, however, would be the sun's ultraviolet radiation. Dr. Carl Sagan and Dr. Philip H. Abelson contend that no bacteria could survive the sun's full rays. Even spores that were shielded by being "locked up" inside a meteorite would be killed by its mounting heat and radioactive elements, as it approached incandescence. The discovery of dead spores—or fossils—of this sort has been claimed by Professor B. Nagy of Fordham University and Dr. George Claus of New York University. Crushing small samples of a rare type of meteorite known as carbonaceous chondrites, in water or glycerol, the two men dropped the samples on glass slides and scrutinized them under a microscope. In three samples, they discerned large numbers of what they described as "organized elements" which they thought might be microfossils having an extraterrestrial source. Some authorities—including Dr. Urey—have been seriously impressed by these findings; but the majority of experts have been skeptical, because the carbonaceous chondrites are very porous and could easily absorb bacteria from the hands of anyone touching them. The meteorites have been here long enough to have been exposed to many kinds of mundane contamination—or so runs the counterargument. Anyhow, these spores are merely fossils—they are dead. They would only indicate the fact of minute life elsewhere in the universe.

Arrhenius expressed his belief that life is a kind of energy which drifts between the stars and galaxies, a cosmic phenomenon like light, and like light it descends ephemerally on those fit to experience it. But this is only a mystical and religious statement from a scientist.

The algae of which we do have fossil traces were very probably preceded by a kind of bacterium, the Leptothrix, a microbe in the shape of a rod, with slender, hairlike cells, which dwelt in the Pre-Cambrian soft-water seas. The Pre-Cambrian era takes us back about fifteen thousand million years, or before the generation of life. The latest guess is about three billion years from bacteria to man, one of a wide range of such guesses. The earliest transitions might very well have been the most difficult and taken longest. From the Leptothrix to the Cyanophyceae or blue algae, for example; and then from the blue algae to the green algae. Our remote ancestor the Leptothrix has not vanished; it is still found in reddish swamps and streams, those in which the water has a high content of iron oxide. Existent also are the Cyanophyceae, or blue algae, and the green algae. Biologists separate animal and plant or vegetable life in the following way: animals possess hemoglobin, and plants possess chlorophyll. Hemoglobin is blood and is formed around an atom of iron. Chlorophyll, that marvelous green agent, is formed around an atom of magnesium. Some arthropods and mollusks, particularly snails, have neither iron nor magnesium but an atom of copper, instead. What was the means of transition, if any, from one form to another? In his popular book, Du Noüy dramatized the mystery of this. Even today there are very elementary kinds of life which elude classification in any group. Among them are the dinoflagellates, also described by Du Noüy, another rather mystical savant. The dinoflagellates cannot be seen by the naked eye, but stagnant water under the miscroscope reveals a swarm of them. They are very agile: swim, leap, and turn. They have exceedingly supple tails, and they appear to breathe: at least, they inflate and deflate their cellular bodies. A red ocular point is sensitive to light and hints at their having rudimentary vision, but that is not certain. They belong to the magnesium group. Where do they fit in the evolutionary scale? Are they to be considered plants or animals? Du Noüy tells us that biologists cannot answer this.

Somehow or other, however, the earliest organisms made their appearance. Scientists do not know in what exact order. Some did not yet have chlorophyll, but instead a pigment called phycocyanin. The Cyanophyceae or blue algae were asexual, also. Then came the green algae, with a nucleus, and both the need and ability to reproduce sexually. Individuality was finally established—the unique birth and death of units of life. No one can determine if the green algae derive from the blue algae, which are asexual and have no nucleus; and if they do, how this momentous advance was performed. Laboratory workers with microscopes speak of evolution, but they only say approximately *what* happened; they stutter or fall silent when asked to explain *how,* or even *why.* (This is similar to Hoyle's comment on the physicists' failure to account for the omnipresent law of gravity.) It is more of a leap, we are given to understand, from the infinitesimal bacteria to the green algae than from those algae, which had the first cellular structure, to us.

(A respected German bacteriologist, Dr. Heinz J. Dombrowski, claims to have revived dehydrated and denatured bacteria that have been imprisoned in varied examples of rock salt since the Permian, Devonian, Silurian, and Pre-

Cambrian ages, altogether a span of six hundred and fifty million years! In many experiments, he has produced saline broths in which he finds living bacteria which he is sure have survived from those remote periods in the exceedingly ancient salt. Such bacteria, later injected into mice, were still potent enough to kill the mice in twelve hours. The microscopic organisms do not feed on the same carbohydrates that are used by similar bacteria today. These claims are still being considered. Although the German scientist has described the elaborate precautions he has taken to prevent any modern bacteria from entering his sterilized nutrient broth, this does not rule out the possibility that he has erred in some way; or that the rock salt itself, while deeply underground, might not have been contaminated through microscopic fissures in its crystalline mass. Yet the weight of the evidence currently seems to lie with Dr. Dombrowski. Although the rock samples have been discovered far inland, the bacteria supposedly sealed in them are of a type usually found in the sea, and in some instances the brine also yielded fossil pollen from trees that grew in the Permian.)

A general opinion amongst biologists is that we may be descended from Pre-Cambrian sandworms. That reminds us of the Samoan creation myth, which also has man coming from worms and maggots. The adaptation of the Pre-Cambrian sandworms was so perfect that they ceased changing. They were probably not very different from some on our shores even now. But one of these worms was less well adapted and continued to evolve. This one, less perfect of his kind, might have been our forefather. He might have been the true Adam, not merely of a new species of worms, but of humankind.

Naturalists proudly make no allowance for a vitalistic principle of any sort. Laboratory workers never permit themselves to talk—as sober scientists—of miraculous intervention. Everything is to be explained in terms of biological mechanisms: adaptive radiations, speciations, specializations. Evolution is simply the rise of the living but material entity through an increasing complexity of organization. To most biologists, there are no signs of a "plan" in all this, and while there are some hints of a "direction," it cannot always be discerned. Natural history merely shows millions of false starts, millions of discards. One eminent paleontologist sees only an "insensate opportunism" and "odd randomness" in the whole process, fitting no purpose, giving no indication of a goal.

A classic example of the working of nature is what has happened on an island in the East Indies, in the Straits of Sunda, where the great volcano of Krakatoa erupted about sixty years ago. All the island's flora and fauna was destroyed. Twelve months later, a French botanist courageously crossed the widespread lava and saw only one sign of life anywhere, a little spider which had very likely been blown there by the salt wind. A few years later, some algae appeared; nothing else could endure in the still smoldering lava and ashes which covered everything. The algae went to work, however, and before long there was soil. In two decades, the once-devastated island was habitable. Earthworms came with an ocean-borne rotting tree trunk, and driftwood from other islands brought a hardy species of lizards. In the same fashion, most likely, our entire earth was conquered by sea plants and creatures millions of years ago. One difference, a great one, is that the algae, earthworms, lizards, and sea vegetation creeping over the lava crust of Krakatoa were already developed forms or organisms, whereas the primeval forms were still in very early stages.

Today there are about eight hundred thousand different kinds of insects, and about a quarter of a million other kinds of living creatures; and perhaps five million forms in all, most as yet unclassified. (The *Upanishad* hymn of the conjugating Lord of the Universe and his reluctant mate—quoted in my first chapter—might still serve as an elaborate allegory of this cellular multiplication or proliferation.) The rate of evolutionary change has not been constant or progressively more rapid, but instead—if fossil remains are a true guide—has fluctuated considerably. Perhaps climate has been a factor, but not a dominant one, since it is too local and erratic. Even the ice ages affected only some species, but had no influence on others.

III

Simpson, one of our most respected living authorities, says that from the tree shrew to something like the primitive ape is only thirty million years. But then again, as the late Sir Charles Sherrington points out, it took conservatively a hundred million years to evolve the principle of the hinge mechanism of the elbow. Each person's elbow can last about three score years and ten, but it can repeat itself to pattern, which is another mystery that no naturalist can explain.

A familiar story concerns a debate between Bishop Wilberforce and Thomas Huxley, who was Darwin's earnest advocate. The Bishop asked whether Huxley was boasting of descent from an ape on his grandmother's or his grandfather's side. To this, Huxley replied that he was descended from the ape on both sides, but sought to discomfit the worthy Bishop by reminding him that at one time he was a speck of jelly no larger than the tip of Huxley's pencil. The fact is, both contestants were partly mistaken. We are now told that man and ape are only distantly related; they are cousins some degrees removed. According to anthropologists, there are four separate lines of primates. All of them radiate from the first, the prosimians, such as the Madagascar lemurs and aye-ayes. The second line is the ceboids, which include the South American monkeys; and the third, the cercopithecoids, the Old World or African monkeys, which include the macaques. Man belongs to the hominoid group, which is the fourth line, and so does the ape. Just as the hominoids result from a radiation of the prosimians, man is a radiation of the hominoids, in the Miocene period. The natives of Madagascar, in choosing the lemur and aye-aye as their totems, have the latest scientific theory to back them up. They are actually kin to the lemur, and their immediate forefather and ours is probably the tree shrew, as was indicated above. The aye-aye is really a "higher" development than man in some ways; that is to say, it is far more distant from its ancestral condition as a prosimian. Simpson asserts that other lines have diverged and specialized as the gibbons, orangutans, chimpanzees and gorillas, following paths involving no competition with one another or with early man. Other ancient lives, near one or the other of these at various phases of their history, vanished as the successful types prevailed. Such a one was Neanderthal man, not an ancestor of ours, but a member of a different family which long since became extinct. The Neanderthalers were dominant over Western Europe for probably hundreds of thousands of years before and during the last great glacial period.

North America may have seen other early types of men, such as Sandia man and Folsom man, both now extinct, too. Thirty thousand to twenty-five thousand years ago, they existed here, which would make them almost contemporary with European Cro-Magnon man. But only caves and tools and spear points have been found in North America, no skeletal material; so, very little is known about such ghostly progenitors of ours. The nearer the paleontologists approach to the present, the more dubiety there is. They think that they can follow the rise of man's more remote vertebrae ancestors with enough certainty up to the point where the primates come upon the scene. From there on, scientists lose the trail in a maze of fragmentary fossil remains, many of which look like man, but not enough so to have their sure place in his history.

Toynbee tells us that the general opinion is that human life has been on this planet for at least six hundred thousand years, and perhaps for a million years. Mammals, says Du Noüy, are about twenty to thirty million years old. Such figures, giving man enormous antiquity, are little contested today; and Dr. Henri Vallois, of the Musée de l'Homme in Paris, declares that man's split with the rest of the animal kingdom may even have taken place sixty million years ago. "The precise location in time of the beginning of human evolution depends upon which primate beast is assumed to be man's closest ancestor." If man is descended from the tarsier, a little tree monkey still found in the East Indies, his age will be the highest possible one; but if his line of descent is from the lemur—as Simpson and others believe—his age is less than one million years. Vallois offers twelve different theories such as these, and decides that all of them are plausible. This is as much as to say again that nothing is known. By Biblical count, the world of man is only a little over fifty-seven hundred years old; but an ancient Japanese myth relates that from the reign of Ninigino-Mikoto, grandson of the Sun-Goddess, to that of Jimmu Tenno, the first emperor, one million, seven hundred and ninety-two thousand, four hundred and seventy years elapsed. This is a computation singularly in accord with the best academic opinion, though I hardly intend that weight should be attached to the coincidence—or some of the others I have mentioned.

The first-known representatives of our own species appear suddenly in the Upper Pleistocene, by which time their form differs from ours hardly more than we differ amongst ourselves. This is during the ice age. Dr. S. L. Washburn, of the University of California at Berkeley, declares from fossil evidence that within a comparatively short span in the Pleistocene, the capacity of the human skull grew tremendously. Within a few thousand years it doubled from a skull capacity of a pint and a half, like the apes, to a capacity of the three pints of modern man.

Britton theorizes that when the glaciers crept down, the ape men walked upright instead of on all fours, to keep their bellies and hands from getting cold and wet. Their erect posture caused a greater flow of blood to the brain, and so their brain grew larger. Britton has tested this hypothesis on chimpanzees; in cold weather they rear up, and the increase of blood to the head is measurable.

A later but similar guess, put forward by Sir Allister Hardy of Oxford University, is that man derives from apes who were driven to hunt in the sea for food by fierce competition in the forests. Sir Allister maintains that the development resulting from life in the shallow coastal waters about a million years ago accounts for the relatively slight body differences between men and apes today. At first the apes waded and groped, then gradually learned to swim. After thousands of years, the species lost its hair, in the same way as whales; except that hair still covered the head, possibly as protection against the sun. Because the water supported the body, and they wanted to swim, they developed longer legs than the land ape. By having to feel along the sea bed for food and to pry open crabs, their hands lengthened and straightened and became more sensitive. By seizing stones on the beach to crack open sea urchins, they took a first step in the use of tools. After a very extensive experience of seashore life, ape man, his posture erect, his legs longer, his hands agile, his brain enlarged, was now ready to re-enter and reconquer the forests and plains, hunting and giving chase to the other beasts there.

One very notable recent discovery, a disconcerting one for some scientists, is of fossils of two kinds of man apes in South Africa. They are the australopithecines and are what people like to call the "missing link." Their characteristics are intermediate between the true forest apes and Java man. They are short, about four feet tall, and weigh about eighty pounds. They had brains three times as large as that of the baboon and considerably bigger than that of any adult chimpanzee, and had humanlike teeth and walked erect. They employed the bones, teeth, and horns of other animals as tools before chipped or flaked stones came into use; and apparently they practiced cannibalism, slaughtering one another with bone clubs and daggers of antelope horn. (They are not yet toolmakers, but with dawning intelligence utilize whatever natural implement is scattered about.) The difficulty in classifying them is from their geological time, which is too recent; before they appeared, the same evolutionary trends had already produced Homo sapiens elsewhere. If their fossils could be ascribed to an earlier period, they would almost certainly be placed in the human line of ancestry; but as it is, they seem more like an independent start in the human direction, one which was made too late and succumbed. This suggests that a new line of man was started on its way after we—the crown of the evolutionary process—had reached our present form, and also that this newer line gave out. What will be the effect of this discovery on all the Evolutionary theorists who believe in the self-flattery of "telefinality" or something like it? That evolution has reached its goal in us? Many such questions tempt us. Why did Neanderthal man fail? Why did

Homo sapiens survive? Why, afterwards, did the australopithecines appear and fail? Will the natural order try once more? Will there be a new species to rival us some day?

Another point in dispute amongst naturalists is whether man's progenitor was a pygmy or a giant. Formerly, it was assumed that in its descent the human frame has constantly grown larger; one of the chief features of the evolutionary process is supposed to be an increase in the total amount of living matter. But Dr. Ralph von Koenigswald, a Dutch paleontologist, has gathered some massive teeth and jawbones from eroded stone in Java which seemingly once belonged to monstrous manlike creatures eight to nine feet tall and weighing six hundred to seven hundred pounds. They were four times the size of present man. In China, too, great teeth have been found, larger than those of a gorilla, which indicate the existence of some giant man. Weidenreich has revised the whole chronology of human evolution as a consequence of these findings, and names the huge Gigantopithecus as man's earliest known ancestor, about a half-million years ago. Von Koenigswald supposes that man, whose first habits were probably arboreal, finally got too heavy to swing from tree to tree. The branches snapped under him too often, and he took to the ground. For protection, he armed himself with a stone axe, and with less stretching exercise shrank to his present smaller size.

But how much data inspires all this conjecture? Exceedingly little. A handful of teeth, a few skulls, and a dozen jawbones and thighbones . . . not a complete skeleton. The paleontologist's method was brilliantly vindicated, however, when Peking man was found in a "dragon-bone" cave at Choukoutien about forty years ago. First a single tooth was unearthed, and on the basis of that the whole skull was described, and then an ape-like jaw was picked up, and then an actual skull, which did fit the picture constructed from the first discovered tooth. The skull is that of a young adult, with distinct sutures. Since then many more jawbones have been found. Peking man was short, about a foot less than modern man, and his brain capacity was twenty percent smaller than ours. He was a toolmaker, obviously a cannibal, and perhaps talked a few words. From all the signs which a research worker takes as conclusive, Peking man lived a half-million years ago and hence was contemporary with Von Koenigswald's giant Java ape man. Both of them are older than Neanderthal man. Koenigswald later put back the date of Java man to even earlier in time, but the tendency of other scholars has been in the opposite direction. The giant creatures are said to have flourished only two or three hundred thousand years ago.

Yet they become comparatively modern figures, when compared to Oreopithecus, "Tuscany man." Twenty-six bone fragments were found in a coal mine in Italy, south of Pisa. They were studied by Dr. Johannes Huertzeler, a Swiss, who ascribed them to twelve different examples of "Tuscany man," once dismissed as a man ape, but now deemed by Dr. Huertzeler to be a forerunner of man himself. Subsequently, Dr. Huertzeler found a nearly complete skeleton embedded in coal in the mine six hundred feet below the surface. Unlike Gigantopithecus, but like the australopithecines, "Tuscany man"—to judge from his skeleton—seems to have been only four feet high. If a human progenitor, Oreopithecus would date our line back ten million years, a huge stretch, far in excess of any other estimate of man's ancestry. But some paleontologists believe that he is, like Neanderthal man and the South African australopithecines, another branch which started and completely died out long ago. The final scientific opinion has not yet been stated.

Elsewhere in Africa, in the snake-infested Olduvai Gorge in Tanganyika, Dr. Louis Leakey, an indefatigable searcher, has found the skull and shinbone of an eighteen-year-old youth, who is now known as Zinjanthropus (East African man, or Nutcracker man, since he had huge bone-crushing molars). The gorge was once a lake bottom. The skull was in four hundred and fifty fragments that had to be pieced together. First estimated by Dr. Leakey as "more than six hundred thousand years old," Zinjanthropus has since been determined by University of California geologists, who applied a radiochemical form of dating that uses argon and potassium, to belong to a past period more nearly one million seven hundred and fifty thousand years ago. As a consequence, Dr. Leakey insists that Zinjanthropus is by far the oldest "true man" yet discovered. He stood absolutely upright. This claim is made, although only the shattered skull and shinbone remain. In general, Dr. Leakey's supposition is accepted by his fellow experts. Dr. Leakey further conjectures that the youth died a natural death from pneumonia, on the shore beside the cool, rainy African lake, abounding with fish and crocodiles, during an era when Europe and North America were sheathed by glaciers. This does not end Dr. Leakey's imaginative conjecturing: the youth apparently died "at home," surrounded by the crude stone tools he used and the bones of small animals his species had just begun to feed on: mice, snakes, and lizards. After his death, his mourners covered him with thornbrushes to prevent his being eaten by hyenas. In life, the boy had an extremely long, wide face and almost no forehead. He stood not quite five feet tall, had a massive chest and shoulder muscles, but spindly legs. At least, Dr. Leakey says the shape of certain parts of the skull shows evidence that massive muscles were attached to it. (Question: from one shinbone, can one "reconstruct" a leg?) Since Zinjanthropus was a toolmaker, a fashioner of very primitive artifacts, this does move man's origin three times further back than the origin of any other known "true man."

Two years later, in 1961, Dr. Leakey came upon what might be even older remains; that is, the bones were buried in a lower rock stratum of the Olduvai Gorge. Dr. Leakey believes they once belonged to an eleven-year-old child and an adult, both of undetermined sex. The newly found relics include the child's skull, part of the hands and foot, the greater part of the jaw of the adult, and a collarbone, hand, and an entire foot. They were also tested for age by Evernden and Curtis, the same two geologists at the University of California.

Just as Dr. Leakey diagnosed the cause of Zinjanthropus' death—pneumonia—even though he had only a skull and shinbone to go by, he has pronounced that this lower-buried child was murdered: in its skull is a sizeable hole with fracture lines in it. This rules out, for the finder, the possibility that the child fell or was struck by a falling branch, for there were no trees or cliffs in the neighborhood at that time; therefore, "I think we can take for granted," Dr. Leakey says, "that the child was hit on the head by a blunt instrument."

Evernden and Curtis later fixed the date of some of Leakey's finds, of prehuman creatures, at fourteen million years, in the Lower Pliocene. Somewhat later, Dr. Elwyn L. Simons of Yale reported the discovery in North Africa, southwest of Cairo, of remains of a "common ancestor" to man and most apes, Propliopithicus, whose date is thirty-three million years—based on jaw fragments only. He also cited new studies of animal remains in Burma of Pondaungia, a monkeylike creature the size of a cat, some forty million years old, who might have been the progenitor of both the Egyptian Propliopithicus and the gibbon apes (although it is a long distance from Burma to North Africa).

But here let us pause a moment. Can a whole species

always be presumed to resemble a few fragments? Can one skull and thighbone, ten or fourteen or thirty-three million years old, or a dozen skulls and a crateful of very ancient bones, be considered the archetypes of an entire group? I have a friend who is short, perhaps five feet five inches. Another good friend stands six feet two. They belong to the same species, assuredly, but at least in size their skeletal remains would be very different. From that kind of proof, would a savant a few million years from now pronounce on whether our race was large or small? How can Dr. Leakey describe Zinjanthropus as an eighteen-year-old, or the "murdered child" as an eleven-year-old (sex unknown), without having many other remains with which to compare them? For how does anyone know from such spare remains what this species of man or sub-man was really like?†

To give another example: for nearly a decade, excited announcements were made about Proconsul africanus, based on some smashed and weathered bits of skull and limb bones discovered near Lake Victoria in Kenya. All sorts of elaborate reconstructions of his appearance and activity were published. Supposedly he lived in the Miocene

---

† Indeed Dr. Leakey has changed his mind once again—since this book went to press—and now believes that Zinjanthropus was "an australopithecine, a nonhuman vegetarian of low intelligence and not a toolmaker." His newest candidate as man's ancestor is a four-foot pygmy, Homo habilis, a fossil more recently found in the Olduvai Gorge. This enthusiastic scientist hypothesizes that Homo habilis may have killed and eaten the dull-witted Zinjanthropus, whose bones were nearby.

Some critics have said that Dr. Leakey's finds are not of new species at all. A further difficulty for him is his latest discovery of three completely different manlike creatures and tools of separate cultures in the same rock-bed. Apparently the three had not succeeded one another but instead had co-existed. "Obviously," a helper of his admits, "the situation is very much more complex than we had dreamed."

period, twenty-five million years ago, and had more manlike characteristics than apelike ones, suggesting that the human line was actually older than the ape line. But then bones of Proconsul's forearm and hand were found and spoiled the theory, for they indicated that their owner had swung by its hands from bough to bough. So Proconsul was apparently an ape, perhaps a forefather of modern apes, but not of nonbrachiating man. Or again, when a skeleton of Neanderthal man was fitted together in 1911, no allowance was made for the bones having belonged to an old Neanderthaler who suffered from arthritis. His stooped posture, therefore, was a considerable distortion. He is now thought to have stood as erect as modern man.

Archaeologists and paleontologists have a variety of skills and methods to help them. They use stratigraphy and typology; they date the age of a "find" by the geological stratum or rock level in which it is turned up, and they correlate and classify the artifacts—handiwork such as spearheads, arrows, shards of pottery, stone talismans—with others of a like style dug up elsewhere. They apply the "fluorine test," since fluorine increases measurably with the passing of time. Another technique is dendrochronology. The age of wood can be determined by studying the sequence of growth rings in it. An even newer and more promising device is the assessment of the decay rate of radioactive carbon content of charred remains, when these come to hand. Thus, very recently, the date of Stonehenge (the ancient megalithic monument in Britain) was changed when some Edinburgh scholars uncovered two new holes in which some of the stones originally stood. One of them had been used as a ritual pit and contained fragments of burnt wood. The dead ember was sent to a scientist at the University of Chicago, who determined that it was about thirty-eight hundred years old (his margin of error, either way, was two hundred and seventy-five years). Similarly, the age of Cro-Magnon man has lately been lessened by as much as thirty-five thousand years as the result of the analysis of charred human bones by this carbon-dating technique.

Unfortunately, it is not often that burnt bones and wood are dug up. Such "finds" are bound to be most exceptional, and who knows how old the remains already were before they were charred? (For instance, there is at present a rumor that, as a consequence of the war in China, the bones of Peking man—taken from the museum—have been consumed by hungry Chinese as a rare and highly esteemed delicacy. If this is true, they will have undergone still another metamorphosis!) Also, a study of tree rings could set a minimum age but never a maximum one, since it will tell how long the tree lived but not how long it has been dead. As for stratigraphy, it must be obvious that to judge the age of teeth and thighbones from their place in geological levels is highly unreliable guesswork. A good many local and eccentric factors must have entered into rock formation, influenced by climate and stream erosion. Earthquakes and flash floods. Volcanic flows, rock slides. What if winds and storms later scooped out caves, or the bodies of the dead were interred in deep graves which reached earlier strata? Would not the sum of all such accidents, and many others, result in virtual uncertainty?

The carbon-dating technique is effective in exploring a past span of not more than fifty or sixty thousand years (some say only forty thousand). Lately its accuracy even within that scope has been challenged, because it assumes a consistent and equal flow of cosmic rays during all periods; whereas there are good indications that the rate at which the top of earth's atmosphere has been bombarded by the rays has varied considerably from century to century, with the result that the production of carbon 14 has also varied.

This is the contention of Dr. T. A. Rafter of New Zealand's Institute of Nuclear Sciences, who states that the abundance of carbon 14 has actually been rising steadily due to the increasing intensity of cosmic-ray activity. Dr. Rafter, citing experiments on an eight-hundred-year-old kauri tree, or New Zealand pine, says that all presently accepted datings are off by as much as fifteen percent. An object set at A.D. 1200 should instead be placed at A.D. 1390. (Other ways in which carbon 14 datings can be wrong will be referred to on a subsequent page.)

We have also had a conspicuous example of error in Dr. Leakey's first attributing an age of "more than six hundred thousand years"—based on stratigraphy—to Zinjanthropus, only to learn by the most modern of all tests—the radiochemical—that Zinjanthropus's birth and death most probably occurred not less than one million seven hundred and fifty thousand years ago. This is a gross error of about three hundred percent, in fixing a date by stratigraphy; but no doubt Dr. Leakey was delighted to be proved wrong in his first estimate, since it now gives his "find" that much greater antiquity. The method used here, by Drs. Evernden and Curtis, is one of several that observe the rate of radioactive decay of substances in rocks. It proves most effective in determining great ages, usually a span of more than one million years. Sometimes rubidium 87 is studied, sometimes potassium 40, or uranium 235, or uranium 238, or thorium 232. In the instance of Zinjanthropus, the amount of change from potassium 40 into argon 40 was measured in rock specimens taken from the strata in which the skull had been embedded. Each rock sample sent from Tanganyika was dissolved in molten sodium hydroxide to liberate the argon 40 in it, this argon being the radioactive decay product of the potassium 40 contained in the sample. But Evernden and Curtis announced, along with their result, that their findings are possibly quite invalid; they have no assurance that mineral deposits, much older than the Tanganyika rock specimen, might not long since have contaminated it. The age set by the tests, when applied to bone remains dug out of that strata, could easily be negated. It is only a possible date, scarcely a definite one. This was a point not generally appreciated by the lay public.

IV

By the end of the nineteenth century, a good deal of Darwin's Theory of Evolution was considered outmoded by naturalists, though the public was not aware of that, either. In fact, the theory had hardly yet begun to convert the layman at a time when scientists were already becoming more critical of it and rejecting many of its tenets. This "cultural lag" between the opinions and information of experts and the credulity of the public is a frequent occurrence. Darwinism is a notable instance of it.

Too much of Darwin's theory appeared to naturalists to be catch-as-catch-can; too much of it relied on the fortuitous. According to the author of the theory, slight changes, adaptive ones, keep the species alive. A new environment, particularly a hostile one, calls forth a series of slight variations accumulated by natural selection. Such gradual change would seldom provide for survival, though; in too many instances, the change would be far too slow; the species would never reach its goal. So workers in this field supplanted Darwinism with neo-Lamarckism.

But alas, neo-Lamarckism is based on fallacious genetics; acquired characteristics cannot be transmitted. To replace it, Weissmann's neo-Darwinism was soon introduced. Naturalists now emphasized natural selection to the exclusion of almost every other factor in evolution. But Weissmann's popularity amongst scientists was short-lived. Next came De Vries and his discovery of sudden mutations. Some changes are not gradual and adaptive, as Darwin had confidently stated; some appear to be spontaneous and accidental. No one knows what causes such abrupt mutations; perhaps they are brought about by ionizing radiations, even from cosmic rays. (Experiments with fruit flies, when they are exposed to X rays, tend to bear this out.) Darwin was half a Lamarckian, and his knowledge of genetics was slight. So an earnest revision of theories was in order again. There has since been no lack of former ones altered and new ones enthusiastically offered. All this is excellent: science should never become dogmatic or complacent, and it must dutifully absorb all new facts and findings. What should be clear to the lay reader, however, is the tentative nature of scientific knowledge.

We learn that, after some years, Darwinism is momentarily back in favor again. Natural selection has been chosen to act as an arbiter amongst the mutants, to decide which shall continue and which shall perish: an idea that was first broached by Empedocles. Nowadays, too, recombination through crossbreeding is recognized as still another impetus to change. Much depends, we are told, on which genes are dominant and which recessive. Mutations seem to involve chance, therefore, and crossbreeding and natural selection are also dependent on many fortuitous circumstances. Indeed, there is an implication that the governing factor in evolution is largely chance. We begin to wonder if chance alone has produced such complicated things as the human brain or eye. Or the delicately balanced chemistry of the vascular system? Would not thousands of fortunate chances be required, an incredible number of them? In fact, statistically, a quite impossible number?

Today there are many scientists and philosophers who

differ in their approach to evolution. To mention a few: Bergson and his *"élan vital,"* Buis and his "cellular consciousness," Rosa and his "hologenesis," Du Noüy and his "telefinalism," Berg and his "nonogenesis," Diresch and his "entelechy," Osborn and his "aristogenesis." Some argue for "orthogenesis," a belief that evolutionary progress is in a straight line. Others have theories filled with teleology; they perceive an over-all design incorporating every aspect of the world, even though the natural scene offers so many elements which appear to be dysteleological and the works of evolution often seem haphazard, purposeless.

Very long books, filled with countless observations and facts about plant and animal life, have been written by naturalists. Books of this kind are truly fascinating. Julian Huxley, for one, has compiled a study of the toilet habits of birds, how some fledglings are taught to defecate over the edge of nests, to keep them clean. Such behavior is proof of the social intelligence of birds. But this intelligence at work also adds to the mystery of nature, and we find that Darwinism is but a superficial explanation of all that has to be accounted for, if we are to grasp the true processes of selection, development, and change.

For example, what is the significance of the male robin's red breast? And why does he have a´special stiff, erect pose which displays his color more prominently during the mating season? Darwin says this is to attract the female robin. Julian Huxley holds that this conspicuousness has more purposes than one: the color and the posture of the robin are also a threat to other male birds, who might be sexual rivals. But is this not an inverted argument? I find it hard to be persuaded by either Darwin or Julian Huxley. Can we suppose that in the course of evolution a robin "develops" a red breast in order to attract a female and frighten a rival? By what means is that brought about? Is not the very opposite likely? Could not the female be attracted to the red because that hue is associated with the male bird? The bird's breast is not red to draw the attention of possible admiring mates, but merely red by accident, and the color has gradually become meaningful to the female? Or, if the red is a threat, it has become a warning to rivals in the same way.

But is there any justification for thinking that a robin develops its distinctive color only by accident? Is a bird's hue actually purposeless? We behold everywhere the marvels of protective coloration. In Africa, there are moth cocoons which birds devour, but some of the cocoons have tiny white parasites on them that the birds find unpalatable, so they leave them alone. In that region, however, the cocoon of one species of moth is marked with white spots exactly like those infested with the parasites, and its decoration serves to keep off the birds, which are deceived and avoid it. Is that merely chance? But the over-all "design"—if there is one at work here—is not purely beneficent; for parasites consume the moths, even though birds do not. What system of balances and checks prevails here? Leaf insects and butterflies of all kinds furnish a host of other examples of the same guile "developed" in marking, shape, and color: yet none is ever completely safe. Anyhow, what good does the robin's red breast do him? It does not help him to hide from his foes or frighten them away.

Two American biologists, Roeder and Treat, have sought the baffling secret of the noctuid moth, a species that has demonstrated remarkable skill in eluding bats, its natural enemy. As is now well-known, bats are guided to night-hidden insects by a high-pitched hunting cry—far above the limit of human hearing—that bounces off the bodies of their tiny prey much like sonar impulses, or radar; yet many night-fliers do succeed in escaping them. Working with delicate care, Roeder and Treat attached infinitely thin wires to the nerves leading out of the ears of the noctuid moth and linked them to an amplifier and oscillograph. An electronic generator was turned on that emitted brief bursts of ultrasonic sound, in plausible simulation of a swooping bat. Even when the beeps were too weak to be heard by man-made microphones, the moth's ear responded with electrical signals. When the artificial bat sounded louder, as if it were drawing near, the moth's ear responded more emphatically, and the oscillograph recorded graphs of "wiggly warning lines." Then the test was moved outdoors, at night, where real bats were prowling. From the traces on the oscillograph, still attached by wires to the ear of a moth, the biologists could tell whether an invisible bat was closing in or flying off. With a floodlight and camera, they observed the abrupt and bewildering evasive action taken by other moths; warned and directed by their sensitive hearing of the hunting bat's nearness, they dove sharply into the grass or performed a series of quick turns, climbs, and loops. As a result of such maneuvers, the moth had at least a forty percent better chance of survival, a very high figure compared with the general survival value of other biological characteristics. An astonishing thing, the noctuid moth's ear! How does one account for its origin and growth? Equally marvelous is the bat's cry, that detects and guides it directly to its prey in the blackness. What developed its radar system? The evolutionary theory, as described by Darwin and refined by later naturalists, answers little or nothing in this brambled thicket of questions.

The truth is, naturalists cannot trace without gaps the descent of any known species today. They cannot begin to explain how the gene is translated into the complete organism, or how the invisible germ cell of the ant contains the brain of another ant and a full outline of its bodily structure and its complement of hereditary instincts, including its altruistic and social impulses. Evolution is merely an extremely vague and confused description of the interrelation of the natural world and nature's widespread propensity to change its forms, a process which goes on endlessly. Darwin's theory, purporting to give us the history of present forms of life, depends on laws and generalizations which are enormous oversimplifications. The literature of the naturalists is a mass of contradictions and hiatuses. Our grandfathers were much too optimistic about Darwinism. The more data the evolutionists gather, the more they quarrel with one another. Wherever a belief in divine or supernatural purpose appears in a theory, a mythic quality of thought enters.

V

Civilization's age is another question which concerns us. We do not realize how deep the roots of man's beliefs actually are. Our tendency is to think of the times of the Egyptians, Greeks, and Jews as eras of deep antiquity. Long before that our mental processes were determined. Even while I have been writing this book, three skeletons seventy-five thousand years old have been found in Northern Iran. The reports about them are still not detailed, but these are apparently the oldest human remains ever dug up. They indicate that "modern man" may have existed even before a more subhuman species such as Neanderthal man. The physical structure of the skeletons of the three men located near the Caspian Sea bears a full resemblance to our own. The chief difference is that the brain chamber is somewhat smaller, about three hundred cubic centimeters. But before conclusions are reached, it is best to wait and learn whether the first "expert" opinions expressed about these bones are borne out. We have already seen how often errors are made in the early enthusiasm over such finds. That "modern man"—Homo sapiens—coexisted with Neanderthal man, however, is also substantiated by yet another recent discovery of skulls of both species in two caves one hundred feet apart on Mount Carmel in Palestine. These specimens too are thought to be as much as seventy thousand years old, or more; it has been suggested that the two races could have inhabited the same caves, though perhaps not at the same time; or else, they might even have warred on each other. Yet another possibility, which appeals to some anthropologists, is that here there was an interbreeding and consequent hybridization of the two branches of humans. Some skulls do seem to show confusingly mixed characteristics. But this brings us again into the realm of guesswork.

Modern man is clearly related to Cro-Magnon man and Grimaldi man, however. Cro-Magnards lived about thirty thousand years ago, as did the Grimaldis, and apparently both were rivals of the hairy Neanderthalers, who were small-brained (though Eiseley disputes this), without much jaw, and almost speechless. Neanderthalers had stone weapons, but no art. They did observe funerary rituals. Cro-Magnon man was tall and blond, a physical type superior to any group of man since. In height he averaged six feet five. His cranium capacity was even larger than ours. Possibly he came from North Africa. He belongs to a glacial epoch, and roamed at a time when the last continental ice sheet extended over the plains about the Pyrenees and Alps. The ice, retreating from northern Europe, still brightly coated all Scandinavia. He had heat, light, clothing, and developed a superb technique in stonework: his engraved tools and weapons were of bone and ivory. His skill in drawing, painting, and sculpture was so deft and delicate, that Picasso and other contemporary artists of ours delight in imitating or trying to capture the spirit of the

Cro-Magnon cave paintings. Such art is called Aurignacian. The limestone cavern murals at Montignac, in France, come upon by five youths about three decades ago, are magnificently rich in the multicolored symbols of his sympathetic magic. They show how much religion and superstition filled his daily life. Some of our myths probably go back to him. It is hard to distinguish him from Grimaldi man, except that the latter had Negroid features.

Cro-Magnon man lived on game only. About ten thousand years ago, man began to till and raise food cooperatively. Society began to take form. A pre-Sumerian flint sickle about eight thousand years old has been found, perfectly preserved, at Hassuna in Mesopotamia, four hundred miles north of Ur. That scythe of flint spells the end of man's predominant phase as a nomad and the start of his agriculture. Earthenware pitchers, jars, and ewers have also been found at Hassuna, and very even, handmade mud bricks and foundations of homes of two and three rooms, with courtyards; so that we have a picture of domestic life. These were no mere hovels; the rooms were about seven feet square and about eight feet high. Eight thousand years ago, for certain, man was no longer only a tent dweller or a seeker of shelter from storms in caves. Hassuna has individual graves, and human skeletons unearthed there reveal that the brain cavity of man has not enlarged since, and the length of his body is the same. About five thousand years ago, man discovered metals, which gave him tools assuring not only enough food for his needs but a surplus. That made it possible to support a city population of specialized craftsmen, merchants, bureaucratic officials, and clerks. The great civilization of Ur in that era had kings and queens and a hierarchy of nobles; gods and goddesses were worshipped by high priests and priestesses. The ruins of Ur show abundant signs of former art and opulence.

Our picture of the past, elsewhere than in southern Europe and Asia, is very obscure and fragmentary. Osborn believes that a very crude form of civilization began in Ipswich in England a million years ago in the Pliocene and Miocene, or before the first glacial age, but few other savants agree with him. Indeed, as we have learned, not many think the human race is as old as that. No skeletal remains have been found, but there are simple rock implements called eoliths which apparently belong to that exceedingly early period. They may or may not have been artifically formed; that is part of the debate about them. Heidelberg man, who belongs to what is known as the Chellean culture, lived in Germany a possible two hundred and fifty thousand years ago; but some say six hundred thousand years, and some say a mere forty thousand. All that is left of him is a jawbone, but it is a human one, not an apelike one. The artifacts and implements of this period show an incontestable mastery of technique by someone, and possibly it was his. He was, if he existed at all, a predecessor of Cro-Magnon, Grimaldi, and Neanderthal man.

Africa has yielded many tantalizing fossil remains, which have prompted some paleontologists to claim that man originated on that continent. These include Kanam man (a jaw perhaps six hundred and fifty thousand years old), and Kanjera man (a skull possibly three hundred thousand years old), and Florisbad man (a mere eighty thousand years ago.) Possibly when the glaciers advanced, man or his subhuman progenitors took refuge in the grasslands of Africa. Signs of pebble culture about five hundred thousand years past have been found in Algeria, at Ain Hanesh; and, as we have seen, in the Olduvai Gorge in Tanganyika, and to the north in Uganda. Promethean man, a protoman who possibly could use fire, once roamed the Transvaal. Saldanha man has left stone tools eighty miles above Cape Town: crude stone axes.

In North America, no traces have ever been turned up of a subhuman species. This is why it is supposed that man was highly developed by the time he reached here from Asia or Europe, perhaps by means of a land bridge crossing what is now the icy Bering Strait. The seas then may have been two hundred and fifty feet shallower than at present, because so much water was drawn into the continental glaciers. The ages which I have quoted for Neanderthal and Cro-Magnon man are those which were ascribed before the very recent use of measurements of the radioactive carbon content of charred bones and wood—as I mentioned a few pages back, all these dates are on the verge of being moved up considerably; while the carbon 14 datings themselves are constantly being challenged. Simultaneously, the latest trend in anthropology and archaeology is to make man in the Western Hemisphere much older than before. Spearheads have been found in several North American sites which may have a history of eighteen thousand years. Sandia man, whose culture precedes that of Folsom man, might be thirty or forty thousand years old. He dwelt in the mountains of New Mexico, where he left lance or javelin points, marks of fires, and bones of the prey on which he feasted. Only artifacts remain of him; like Folsom man, who also hunted and cooked his food a possible twenty-five thousand years past in New Mexico and Colorado, no physical fragment of him exists; but we do have these signs of him scattered in caves and camp sites in early geological strata. Both races of men fashioned beautiful stone weapons and killed dangerous game: elephants, horses, camels, sloths, and bison.

Dr. George F. Carter of Johns Hopkins University is bolder than other American anthropologists and declares that man in the Western Hemisphere has an interglacial antiquity of at least one hundred and fifty thousand years, or even three or four hundred thousand years. His claim is based on an ingenious study of the stone or other material used in the artifacts, as for example the thickness of the "desert varnish" on spearheads or the amount of lime leached away from shells. But whether man's history can be "clocked" this way is open to question.

Similarly, the carbon 14 dating test itself has been found fallible by some, as we have observed. The variability of cosmic rays is one factor. Besides this, if artifacts or bones in their natural state have been subjected to chemical alteration, by being exposed to alkali washes, they would have less carbon in them and would seem far older than they actually are. In frequent instances, such chemical changes could have occurred, and the results obtained by the carbon 14 technique would be false. Many supposedly certified dates must be reviewed, then. When Dr. Hibben discovered the artifacts of Sandia man and had them tested, he exclaimed: "This is not geological guesswork. It's an exact, mathematical method of dating. Now we have incontrovertible proof." But the possibility exists that Dr. Hibben may have been mistaken.

In Montana, the Yuma people are shown to have a kinship with Folsom man, but they existed somewhat later than his most recent period, about ten thousand years ago. There are also traces of two interesting primordial cultures in California at about this era, the fancifully named Red Heads and Black Bottoms. Seventy-five skeletons have been turned up in a cemetery buried deep in sand on Santa Rosa Island. Three are of giants seven and a half feet tall, though most are of normal-sized Indians. One hundred and twenty-nine skeletons have been uncovered in another burying place nearby. The skulls of the group interred in the sand are colored a brilliant Chinese red. For this, a lasting dye or paint was used. The pelvic bones and lower spines of the second group have been discolored black from the clay surrounding them; apparently their visceras were removed and their abdominal cavities filled with clay, which suggests an odd mortuary custom. Both the Red Heads and the Black Bottoms were found by Orr. He has reconstructed much of their life and religion, which was remarkably advanced by contrast to tribes which followed them on the island. They made beads and barbed spears, and for their rites they even had instrumental music played on little bone whistles.

North American scientists now skip a long period. They have nothing to fill this lapse of time. The remains of Siberian immigrants, perhaps a mere four or five thousand years old, have been dug up by Hrdlička in Alaska. At Ipiutak on Point Hope, on the Arctic Ocean, explorers have outlined a town, of incredible size and mysterious pre-Eskimo culture, with easily discerned mossy traces of long avenues and many home sites. What these ancient Alaskans ate, in that cold waste, is a puzzle, and oddly none of their weapons is extant. But they had leisure enough to produce artistic objects, some of them for no practical purpose, which hints at a tie with some center of advanced culture in Asia, perhaps Japan. In graves, some skulls have eyeballs of ivory with jet pupils inlaid. The corpse's nose is replaced by a birdlike ivory beak. Such effigies are very beautiful. Where did these people come from? Who were they? Why did they vanish?

In the southwestern part of our country, again, the Basket Makers flourished nearly four thousand years ago. But Mexico is the site of the latest explorations that have yielded startling results. Tepexpan man, found thirty-five miles north of the capital, is at least ten thousand years old.

At first it was doubted that any human immigrant from Asia had ever reached so far south in the Western Hemisphere that long ago. But four weapons have been discovered near him which also lie alongside the bones of a mammoth in what might once have been a swamp; they are more nearly twelve thousand years old. The weapons and tools, two arrowheads made of obsidian—volcanic glass—and a fragment of an obsidian knife and a scraper made of black onyx, were obviously used by a prehistoric man to kill and skin his quarry so that he could eat its meat. Even older, perhaps thirty thousand years, is the fossil—the pelvic bone of a mastodon—discovered by Dr. Juan Armenta Comacho at Balsequillo, near Puebla, sixty miles southeast of Mexico City. The remarkable aspect of this fossil is that it is decorated: on it have been scratched drawings of a primitive horse, a camel, and a type of mastodon which was heretofore thought to have been extinct more than one hundred thousand years past. The age of the bone has been corroborated by the Abelson test, yet another means of dating, by measuring protein molecules and their degeneration at a certain rate. That the drawings were not inscribed by later hands is ruled out, because it is stated that only fresh, green bone would have permitted this sort of carving. Besides, along with the decorated bone were unearthed other possible utensils, including an amulet, boring tools, and about five hundred stone tools. Then man did occupy the southern half of the New World much earlier than was formerly supposed.

In the Caribbean and South American regions, pre-Columbian races such as the Mayan and Tairona and Inca have an unknown antiquity. They also seem to have their racial roots in Asia, but this has never been fully proved. At all odds, the Bering Strait is still not very deep, and only fifty miles wide in places, and even today Eskimos frequently cross it on the ice. Whether the people of North and South America first came south from Siberia, or whether some of them came across the Pacific, or even whether they went west on rafts from the coast of Peru to the islands there, continues to be the subject of much speculation and dispute.

V

That long history is ours, and myths are the oldest spoken record of it we have. The only memorial of any kind, indeed, except for a few dead relics. Bones. Broken jars. Shaped bits of flint and obsidian. Something of all that early man experienced is in us, whether or not one takes stock in Jung's "collective unconscious." The actual primordial images which Jung speaks of might not exist, but is it not possible that our minds still have the same intrinsic patterns as those of Cro-Magnon man and Ipiutak man? These three chapters, in which I have briefly reviewed astrophysical and paleontological theories, have been an attempt to show on a very limited scale how inevitably such patterns of thought reassert themselves.

Erich Fromm remarks: "We feel superior to the superstitions of former generations and so-called primitive cultures, but we are constantly hammered at by the very kind of superstitious beliefs which set themselves up as the latest discoveries of science."

18

A CONCLUSION

My readers will shake their heads and say: "Yes, there are some slight resemblances. But science is very different from mythology. Scientists have a 'method,' and they use mathematics and direct and controlled observation to arrive at their conclusions. Mythology has been mere intuition and guesswork on the part of primitive man."

Yet we have just seen that the "data" of the modern astrophysicist are far less definite than is usually realized, which means that the theorizing based on them is often highly eccentric. The very size of the figures offered and played with by the astronomers should give us pause.

When a lady astronomer at Harvard tells us that the count of stars in the heavens is in the zillions, does not the reader share my lack of knowledge of what that connotes? It is a sum so large as to suggest nothing at all to us. Who can actually form a mental image of one zillion, two zillions, ten zillions, a zillion zillions? Like a wise ancient Persian or Hindu, we might prefer to regard such a number as a symbol only of "infinity," of what we do not know; but not as anything factual.

Every year the astrophysicists convene to read papers on their latest deductions, which the newspapers report in full detail. I have been collecting such reports for years, along with my creation myths. As I confessed in my first chapter, I have always found an immense store of poetry in astronomical observation and thinking. To me, the scribbling by mathematicians of abstruse x's and y's on blackboards, to represent vast distances and invisible events, has the same arcane lure as ancient cabalism. It has been excellently said that the x's and y's of science are, in essence, the frolicsome Greek gods and goddesses in their latest disguise.

Our astronomers change their "statistics" very quickly, indeed. For example, Dr. N. U. Mayall of the Lick Observatory and the University of California, recently declared that the sun moves in a circular course around the center of the Milky Way galaxy at a rate sixty-two and one-tenth miles a second less than had been believed, which exposes a possible error of thirty-six percent in former computations of its speed. His new guess is one hundred and nine miles per second. He founds his figure on a study made by him of the radial velocity systems of fifty globular clusters (systems of stars formed into clusters shaped like a globe). He has also decided that the entire Milky Way may weigh only half as much as savants have supposed before.

Professor Fritz Zwicky, of the California Institute of Technology, using a Schmidt telescope on Palomar Mountain, claims to have found luminous "bridges" connecting widely separated galaxies, some of the bridges more than four hundred and thirty thousand trillion miles long. The significance of these "bridges" or filaments of stars, if they exist widely in the heavens—as Professor Zwicky believes —is that they may increase all previous estimates of the amount of matter in the universe. Such a change would affect all calculations as to how the cosmos was formed and how it is developing, since the total mass of matter is a key figure. The "bridges" may also blur the light from all the stars behind them, throwing off astronomers' measurements of how far off those stars are. The whole geography of the universe may have to be revised again.

We have already seen that very recent guesses as to the age of the cosmos vary from two billion to twenty and even sixty billion years! Faced with such a great divergence of opinion, expressed by highly accredited astronomers, how much significance shall we attach to any of it? Then again we are offered the theory of the Cambridge cosmologists that the universe is timeless and had no beginning; it is a phenomenon of "continuous creation."

Theories, too, change as radically as the figures. Professor Jeffreys has now announced that while he does not entirely reject a "catastrophic" explanation of the origin of the solar system, he is beginning to think it is more likely that the planets have been condensed out of great disks of matter composed both of dust particles and permanent gas. Cecilia Payne-Gaposchkin, at Harvard University, has a rather startling suggestion: the sun, as we know it, might be younger than the earth; the earth might never have been part of the sun and perhaps never very hot, but came directly from material that condensed to form both sun and planets. (It is Mrs. Gaposchkin who places the stellar census in the zillions.)

Mathematical computations on a vast scale greatly impress us, but are they accurate? Professor Henrietta Swope, another astronomer at Harvard, locates the center of the Milky Way at a distance of one hundred million billion miles from our sun. An overwhelming figure! But are we to take it literally? We are hardly in a position to judge. Professor Subrahmanya Chandrasekhar, now of the University of Chicago, calculates that the Milky Way galaxy has been expanding for three billion years and will go on doing so for at least nine thousand, nine hundred and ninety-seven billion more. By that time it will be fully relaxed, the stars in it will all have identical velocities, and will begin to slip away like water evaporated from a wisp of steam. Is this a serious scientific prediction? It is. But how seriously shall *we* take it? In any event, it must be placed alongside the mathematical analysis of Dr. David Layzer, of the Forrestal Research Center, Princeton University, who has decided that the ultimate size of the universe before expansion ends will be a million times its present radius, this to occur ten million million million years after the expansion began. The present cosmos, therefore, is only one billionth of its way along its lifetime. Is this right? When Professor Hubble "proves" that certain galaxies are so far away that their light, speeding at one hundred and eighty-six thousand miles per second, takes five hundred million years to reach the parabolic mirror of his telescope, does it not seem to some of us that hypotheses resting on such uncertain "facts" have a very shaky foundation at best? Do they merit the term "scientific"? These staggering figures uncomfortably remind us of that Renaissance divine, Bishop Usher, who with his quill pen arrived at not only the day and year on which had occurred the creation of man, but also the precise hour.

The astronomers offer these theories that are, perforce, actually based on very little evidence. That the ruddy shift on the spectrum means that the galaxies are in flight from an original exploding atom, that new hydrogen can appear from simply nowhere—all this is backed by the most abstruse mathematics which only a handful of highly intelligent people can possibly understand. The layman accepts most of these statements on faith, because the proof which is offered is usually beyond his comprehension.

Astronomical "knowledge" is largely symbolic; it is scarcely empirical. The conditions for precise measurement and observation that apply in the more sober branches of science do not exist in astronomy. We have an impression of knowing much, when actually we know very little. An honest astronomer will not deny that he is only "speculating." As I have said, his are merely daydreams, not unlike those of early man, but far more expensive. The breath of Brahma and Dooadlera is replaced by "new hydrogen." For "new hydrogen" has become the latest savior, in one sense the latest Culture Hero (and it too is immaculately conceived). "Continuous Creation" might be even more appropriately compared to the Mohammedan belief that Allah reconceives the whole cosmos at every instant, every atom of it; or, with our ever doubling universe, to how Yima and his arrow, in the Persian legend, causes the pregnant world to grow to twice its size. I do not assert that Lemaître and Hubble, or Tolman, or Bondi or Gold, are mistaken in their cosmological thinking (though obviously someone is, since they are at variance). But what strikes us is the mythical quality of the astrophysical debate.

The Norse and Icelandic storytellers probably did not

believe literally in their tales of the sons of Borr, nor did the Babylonian priests at first in Marduk's destruction of Tiämat: they offered the cosmic stories as allegorical explanations. Some or most of the laity of their time and after were credulous, undoubtedly; but not more so than today's public, which mistakes the cosmic fictions of astronomy for fact.

II

What of paleontology, the other "creation" science?

Perhaps of all biological theories, evolution is the most widely believed today. The public regards it, too, as a fact rather than as a hypothesis. Many reasons account for this, including the historical one that during the late nineteenth century, an intelligent man felt himself faced with only two alternatives: espousal of evolution, or literal belief in the Biblical story. Few scientific theories have ever been so popularly debated, and by the largely uninformed; since evolution was at first deemed antireligious. To accept it or not involved each man in a deep personal crisis. Even in my boyhood, as I have said, the public controversy went on. Today Darwin's cause is won, with the result that he is presented to children in our schools as a modern Culture Hero.

But to experts, evolution as an explanation of the rise of living forms is still far from satisfactory. Biologists find so many exceptions to the main outlines of the hypothesis, that there is no longer one evolutionary theory but a half dozen, some of them irreconcilable, and none fully adequate. Thus a French authority, Jean Rostand, has very recently written: "I freely admit that my doubts are of a purely intuitive nature . . . yet I cannot convince myself that the mutations we observe have been able, even with the co-operation of natural selection, even with the advantage of the immense periods of time in which evolution works on life, to build the entire world, with its structural prodigality and refinements. I cannot persuade myself to think that the eye, the ear, the human brain have been formed in this way. . . . I discern nothing that gives the right to conceive the profound structural alterations, the fantastic metamorphoses that we have to imagine . . . when we think of the transition from invertebrates to vertebrates . . . from reptiles to mammals."

Too many gaps remain in the lines of descent. Most laymen, lacking a knowledge of biology, fail to appreciate that in large areas of that subject evolution is only a statement of faith by university professors. It is based on fragmentary evidence and more often on pure guesswork, although admittedly the geology and biology professors do not have to speculate as wildly as the astronomers, since much of what they deal with is more visible, less distant.

The tragicomedy of Piltdown man—"Dawn man"—provides an illuminating instance. Long proclaimed as the "most important anthropological find of the century," Piltdown man's place in the human line was attested by world-famed English paleontologists, who ascribed to him an age that ranged from one hundred and fifty thousand years all the way to nine hundred and fifty thousand. When he was finally shown to be a counterfeit, the excuse offered was that such a fraud could only have been concocted by an expert. The unhappy truth proved to be that a mere ambitious amateur was responsible. The forger had combined an ancient human skull with the jaw of an immature ape, only fifty years dead, which he coated with bichromate of potash and iron to make it look older; and he honed down the teeth to change their shape. Even so, it took almost a half century for this important hoax to be exposed.

I have already referred to other widely publicized errors

that have followed when paleontologists and anthropologists became too excited about their "finds." Who can keep abreast of all the latest paleontological guesses about the age of man and the place and course of his descent? It need not greatly concern us, therefore, whether or not the theories which are outlined here prove to be the "final" ones; they will surely not be for long. That, indeed, is a part of what this book means to suggest. Theorizing about the origin of things goes on endlessly and is influenced by age-old habits of man's imagination. The history of science is as involved, offers as many variants of the same fundamental motifs, as does the history of cosmic myths. At best, we have extended the scientific "method" to realms—astronomy and paleontology—where it works imperfectly; and when the "method" breaks down there, a measure of mythical thinking takes over from it. It happens without the rest of us, or sometimes even the savants themselves, being aware that this is so.

To conclude: the cosmological hypothesizing of our astronomers is in significant part fantasy. The little information which is gained by stargazers at our observatories tells us nothing at all of how the world began. The paleontologists tend to be overenthusiastic and on occasion personally biased in attributing importance to the fossils and bones they fancifully reconstruct. Time and again, they have peopled the past with wholly fictitious species of mankind's progenitors. Besides this, such noted anthropologists as Le Gros Clark and Professor William K. Howells of Harvard University have pointed out how prejudiced is the subconscious of men who study their own evolution.

In defence of science, we must recall how young it is in the long and aspirant span of human history. Someone has very vividly put it that "some eighty to ninety percent of all scientists who have ever been, are alive now." But its very youthfulness as a discipline should make us cautious of its most positive declarations.

It might be said (though I believe the point is quite arguable) that myths tend to persist in the face of incontrovertible fact; they are seldom if ever put to the test of reality. Scientific theories, on the other hand, pretend to be nothing more than tentative. New "facts" quickly alter them. This second statement is certainly borne out by the history of science. The special value of scientific "theories" —as opposed to any form of mythmaking—is that they inspire research along new lines and hence lead to the discovery of "facts" that sometimes have been hitherto unimagined. This attitude about the tentativeness of scientific theorizing, and a complete readiness to change one's views to fit new knowledge, is held with an almost religious intensity by top-flight scientists, including those in the realm of astrophysics and paleontology. I have not wished to declare otherwise, or to cast doubt on the rigorous intellectual honesty of such men amongst us.

But it must also be acknowledged that not all workers in the scientific field today are truly top-flight or selflessly dedicated; there, as everywhere in the world of human endeavor, many researchers are personally ambitious and vainglorious. Such men, seeking attention and advancement, mislead the public by offering a host of too-hasty assumptions. They are too eager to be the "first" with a new idea. In our time, the public is dazzled by the achievements of science, and hence is uncritical of too much that it hears. And the press is careless in reporting to laymen what is proposed as a mere theory, as distinct from what is substantiated as "factual." I do not say that other scientists are misled by reckless claims of this sort, but the general reader is likely to be.

Moreover, even top scientists are sometimes reluctant to

admit that their theories have been based on errors or have been superseded. Who of us does not like to be "right," and who of us does not aspire to fame? Professor George K. Schweitzer, of the University of Tennessee, has remarked that during the past few decades scientists have not been "discovering" their theories as much as they have been "inventing" them.

But more important—from my point of view—is the public unawareness of how large a role is actually played in scientific hypothesizing by the faculty of intuition. The history of science is filled with instances of noted workers in all fields who testify in their memoirs that a "hunch," a perhaps inexplicable ray of light, suddenly led them to a major discovery. Is it Newton under the apple tree, or Galvani watching his wife cook frogs' legs? Some of these invaluable "finds" seem to have been pure accidents. That many theories have such origins does not really discredit them; and they are doubtless also based on an element of logic and have a background of a thorough "factual" survey as well. But what inspires the author of a scientific hypothesis to choose one route, one direction of approach, rather than another, when many offer themselves with equal persuasiveness to him or confront him with an equal opacity? Whence comes the "hunch," what directs the "ray of light," the seemingly lucky chance that without warning illuminates the right dark path to be followed? The problem is too complex to probe easily. Yet I suspect that in such circumstances the mind of all of us has an innate tendency to follow one path rather than another, amongst many, almost involuntarily. Studies in *gestalt* psychology, as well as a neo-Jungian approach, might be helpful here. In any event, is "intuition" always an infallible guide, and may it not lead us in the same direction—or along a route closely parallel—to myth?

All these factors combine to make scientific theorizing far less objective than it wishes to be, even when the best minds are engaged in it. But this is not widely enough acknowledged.

Says Professor Schweitzer further: "Any number of the scientific concepts we accept today may be simply convenient schemata that impose order upon the experiences we have collected so far. They may have little or no relation to 'reality'. . . . A theory is thus neither true nor false; it simply works or it doesn't. Now it is true that many scientists (including myself) *believe* that their theories closely approximate or correspond to 'reality,' but this is an act of faith, for no 'proof' can be adduced for or against it. . . . The large number of modified or even discarded scientific theories should serve as a useful warning."

My fellow student at college, who subscribed to the literalness of the *Genesis* story, was hardly more trusting—as it turns out—than the well-meaning but incompetent professor who gave us the Planetesimal Hypothesis as though it were a proven fact. This prompts an interesting question. Once a "scientific" theory is discredited, is it any longer "scientific"; or is it to be relegated to the realm of myth to which in essence it belongs? Can anyone set a point in history when the rule of science actually began and the bright-colored reign of myth ended? Shall we say that the eighteenth century was the starting point, or the nineteenth, or even the twentieth? Did the "science of astronomy" begin with Swedenborg, Buffon, or Kant, all of whom held mistaken beliefs about the solar system? Did it begin with Laplace, or Chamberlin-Moulton, or possibly Lemaître? We may ask whether the day shall ever arrive when all "scientific" theories are accurate and in full accord with all the "facts."

My young friend thought that divine revelation has

granted man as much knowledge of the origin of the universe as do our inadequate telescopes and faulty mathematics and geologizing. Some readers will not agree with him, because they feel that an allegorical interpretation of the Biblical story is better than a literal one; but they should be equally hesitant about taking issue with him. The truth is, if one is agnostic about religion, it behooves one to be agnostic about certain branches of science, too.

III

Nowadays there is a tendency amongst rational people to be arrogant about the accomplishments of science, and to disparage the *aperçus* of our predecessors. The average school child knows things of which Galileo never dreamed. That is part of the *illusion* of progress. A little scientific learning is indeed a dangerous thing.

The more insignificant modern man becomes—on his shrinking earth, hardly a cosmic speck—the more arrogant he is. He feels far less humility toward the ever-vaster unknown than his forefathers did toward what was thought to be known in a flat, God-ruled, man-centered universe. Science does not seem to touch man's emotions at all: he loses his religious awe and acquires in its place only a boastful complacency about himself. His intelligence grows, but not his genius.

I would define genius as a combination of inventive mind, poetic aspiration, and awe-filled heart.

Whoever has read the creation tales gathered in this book cannot doubt that, in his myths of the world's beginning, man has shown his true genius. His invention is there; his poetry is given its grandest scope; and his awe is omnipresent. But indeed, that is also true of much of the scientific theorizing we have examined. Scientists are far less dispassionate in formulating laws and expounding theories than is popularly supposed; and many of them are great poets.

We need not be surprised at this, for it is obvious that the mythic is our universal mode of thought. We cannot escape it, apparently.

What has happened in science has also occurred in other fields of intellectual endeavor. For example, that brilliant historian Carl Becker—my late teacher—has shown how the eighteenth-century rationalists, who were the first to make a great effort to free themselves from enslavement to "superstition" and mythical thought processes, were themselves merely replacing one set of myths with another set: the myth of the Golden Age, for one. As we have also noted—and Professor Becker demonstrates—the nineteenth-century romantics smuggled back a whole new and rather flamboyant assortment of myths: the "Noble Savage," racism, nationalism, utopianism, amongst them. Both the concepts of the eighteenth-century *Philosophes* and the nineteenth-century humanitarians were as much founded on a "myth" or a collection of mythical premises as were the beliefs of any of their predecessors.

Jung has remarked that because the true nature of things perpetually vexes the intellect—"reality" remains unknown and is not to be fitted into a formula—the scientific intellect is tempted to put on airs of enlightenment in the hope of banishing the specter for once and for all. A vain attempt. Whether its endeavors are called Skepticism or Positivism, or Realism with a capital letter, there is always a myth hiding behind it, in new and disconcerting garb, which follows an ancient and venerable pattern in giving itself out as an "ultimate truth."

IV

It is not my intent to hold up "myth" as a final answer, either. In some ways, it is not any kind of answer at all.

When we say, at present, that something is "mythical," we are not explaining it, but hardly more than describing it.

We need to know a great deal more about mythology, therefore. It is just as promising a source of "knowledge of the world" as any of the physical sciences, for it is a revelation of the mind of man, of the scientist himself. His knowledge of the world must begin with his self-knowledge. Oddly, as Jung has said, psychology has been the last branch of science to appear and develop, although logically it should have been the first. In particular, mythology as a phase of anthropology and psychology has been neglected. I have quoted a dozen opinions about how myths should be interpreted; it is regrettable that no synthesis of those different approaches has been undertaken.

When I was preparing this book, I was hopeful of getting expert advice. But when I turned to the "specialists," I found their counsel very confusing. In particular, I was criticized for having been too eclectic. How could I pay attention to so many schools of thought? That was their question.

But amongst themselves, the anthropologists held very differing views. "Frazer is now considered archaic," one noted scholar wrote to me, slightingly. Said another: "You've been led astray by Malinowski's unfortunate use of the term 'savages.'" (This expresses a new intention amongst anthropologists to discard any reference to "savages," because they think the epithet is derogatory; they prefer to use "primitives," instead. Is not the popular hope that by trivial semantic changes we can exorcise prejudices and stereotypes one of the pious delusions of our times?) Concerning psychologists, the anthropologists are apt to be even more scornful. "Jung is ludicrously naïve," is a comment that I received.

In turn, I learned that the psychologists tend to have

equal contempt for anthropologists. Freud's disciples dismiss most such fieldworkers as merely superficial observers. At the same time, there are fierce feuds amongst the many schools of psychologists: the Freudians, Jungians, Adlerians, Rankians, and others.

At present, it is certainly a fact that far too much of the research into mythology is being carried out by mystics and pseudo scientists. A more hardheaded study of the subject is urgently needed.

V

Very likely a full and clear grasp of the psychological content of myths will never be ours. Some aspects of them are bound to elude us forever, and especially those elements that supposedly arise from the unconscious.

Jung's emphasis upon the importance of the unconscious leads him, when he speaks about myth, to dismiss the personality of the mythmaker as irrelevant. We need know nothing about the storyteller. His personal life explains nothing.

For Jung, consciousness is isolated and prone to painful errors. What lies beneath consciousness, the collective psyche, is full of healing and redeeming forces. A myth, like a work of art, draws on those healing forces but is like a dream, which has many disguises and never has an explicit meaning. We should not try for an intellectual understanding of a myth—or a work of art—but should merely seek to experience it, and then it acts upon us as it first acted on the mythmaker or artist. In the same way, we should embrace the time-old religious symbols in myths; they too will heal us.

Further, Jung says, a perception of the unconscious is a distinguishing characteristic of the artist, whom we equate with the mythmaker. The artist is aware of the chaos beneath the surface of civilized life and tells us of it. Aeschylus, Euripides, Dante, Shakespeare, Goethe give us glimpses of the wild, horrible, inchoate forces in man. Blake and Wagner draw on mythology and primordial imagery for their nocturnal worlds. The ancient myths provide these artists with the fullest picture of man, including his savage and bestial side. Shakespeare's *Hamlet* and *King Lear* are not too different from the Greek tragedies of *Oedipus Rex* and *Oedipus at Colonus,* which depict man two thousand years earlier. (What we find in the collective psyche, then, is not always healing and redeeming? Granted that it may be, when it supplies us with the exalted religious symbols.)

VI

But must we assume with Jung that myths have emanated to such a large extent from the race's unconscious? Has not much conscious thought gone into them? If so, can we not probe it?

The myth, like a work of art, is probably not produced wholly involuntarily as Jung contends, the image growing as a dream grows. The mythmaker, like the artist, may be better able than most of his fellow men to tap the "collective unconscious," but to fashion a work of art or a popularly accepted legend he must also have a degree of conscious skill and intellectual mastery. The primitive mythmaker must have not only the most "archaic" mind in the tribe, but also the most subtle and advanced: he must combine all those qualities in one: Simply having a gift for tapping the "collective unconscious" does not make a man a mythmaker or an artist (though I think the political leader often thrives on little more than that gift, as does the evangelist). We should observe that nonartists often live in the unconscious far more than artists do. Art brings illumination to both the artist and his audience; that is one of its purposes. It does this by way of myth; and the artist's appeal is to consciousness every bit as much as to its opposite.

Jung's attitude is too narrow and deterministic, much as is Freud's. We have seen that where Jung says myths are not accessible to interpretation, Freud holds that they can be as exactly decoded as dream symbols. Every phrase in a myth has a deeper connotation. We might think that much free play and fantasy contributed to them, too, man's love of storytelling and daydreaming for its own sake. But the Freudians would not admit that the mind's fantasy is ever that free. What seems to be an idle fancy is really not: we hide in it a long suppressed wish.

Does every word in a myth have an inverted significance? Do the images of our desire always come to us in a cunning disguise? That they have a propensity to do this in our musings and reveries and art creation is beyond question, but that it happens as unremittingly as the Freudians assert, is probably more open to doubt. With the poetic and romantic apparatus of their analyses and dream interpretations, the more orthodox and fanatic Freudians have demonstrated that they themselves are highly talented mythmakers. They have formulated a self-consistent system which must, like any other logicized system in the highly inconsistent world of human psychology, be looked upon with suspicion.

VII

I venture my opinion that any myth is partly a product of the free play of man's fancy. But his further motivation for mythmaking is also profound and compulsive. He needs to have the world about him explained, and tries to do this by observing and interpreting the significance—if any—of all resemblances. If things in his environment look alike or act alike, or seem to have a common origin, or occur at the same time, the human mind is quick to link them. The mind then seeks to order them, by comparing them and assigning them hierarchal values of one kind or another, adjudged by their presumed origin or effectiveness. Very often, the only links and values that man can arrive at are fictional, mythical, however pragmatic.

This psychological process, by which the myth is brought to birth and grows, helps to explain why art is so closely akin to it, and why both are so important. Without them, and the presumably "factual" axioms of science, the whole universe falls into anarchy and absurdity, since nothing has meaning for us. And science, too, is based on the intuitive or logical perception of real or fancied relationships (in the scientific realm, the term given to such relationships may be "causality"; and though currently it is not respectable, scientists go on using it just the same).

We cope with life by accepting a meaningful pattern, in part self-woven but mostly borrowed from centuries-old tradition. That pattern in large measure consists of myths. No man lives without some sustaining myths about himself and the world; nor does any society. With religious myths, man peoples his cosmos with gods and demigods and intermediaries to make it a somewhat more friendly place in which to live; and by artistic myths he seeks to analyze and decorate life; or, with grossly incomplete data, he tries to reduce the workings of the universe to "natural laws" so that it is more intelligible to his daunted mind—that is science, which is far from objective.

Man's great systematic philosophies are also partly mythical undertakings. They are to some extent *abstract* myths. The very effort to create a "system" in which the infinite variety of the cosmic scene can be neatly fitted together and comprehended as consistent, is both mystical and mythical. Such philosophies are "mystical," because one of the characteristics of the mystical impulse is its hope and need to unify all that is outwardly or inwardly beheld.

We live in the gloriously *rational* twentieth century, but we may anticipate that the future will look back on much of our science, art, ethics—based on our philosophy and religion—as too often in a class with primitive myth and even savage superstition. Yet this judgment need not be pronounced disparagingly by our children, for they can share with us a very high regard for some of the "primitive tales," in which there is so much noble and aspiring poetry. Nor should we expect that future generations themselves will excel us in rationality. Little in the history of mankind thus far encourages that hope.

VIII

History began with Hecataeus and Herodotus as an elaboration on myths. In twenty-five hundred years, it cannot be said to have greatly changed. Vico observed that men are largely governed by myths in politics, and this was also the opinion of Pareto and Sorel. Lenin learned much from them, as did Mussolini and Hitler, and it is one reason for the fantastic successes of these demagogues in the midst of our supposedly enlightened and sophisticated age. The masses of mankind responded not to what was logical, but to what was primitive and savage and mythically poetic in their oratory.

From the terrible ordeals of our time, then, we should have gained a little wisdom. Have we not learned to hold a less optimistic view of ourselves? Dare we count on man's improving his nature? He does so very slowly, if at all.

We realize at last that the new myths of science do not suffice for the masses of men, only for intellectuals, an elite whose imaginations have an affinity or are trained for abstract thought and mathematics. Any attempt to offer scientific myths to the people, in place of political and religious ones, is certain to fail. This is what the humanists talk of doing, but their concept of human nature is ludicrously shallow and inadequate.

Also, we must not assume that the scientific myths and the religious myths have the same function, even though their psychological processes are akin to some degree. Santayana once put it this way:

> The soft-hearted, the muddle-headed, the superstitious are all raising their voices, no longer in desperate resistance to science, but hopefully, and in its name. Science, they tell us, is no longer hostile to religion, or to divination of any sort. Indeed, divination is a science, too. Physics is no longer materialistic since space is now curved, and filled with an ether through which light travels at three hundred thousand kilometres per second—an immaterial rate. . . . All this I find announced in newspapers and even in books as the breakdown of scientific materialism: and yet, when was materialism more arrant and barbarous than in these announcements? Something no doubt has broken down: but I am afraid it is rather the habit of thinking clearly and the power to discern the difference between material and spiritual things.

Since Santayana spoke out, there is a newer tendency which we should behold with even more alarm: the pseudo-educated laity has faith in science itself, as though it were a god, a personified, wonder-working demiurge. Already it has its martyrs and its band of converts, selflessly consecrated and fanatical.

Our wish to believe in something is part of our compulsion to create myths, even scientific ones about the beginning of the world. That is why the need to study the psychological roots of myth is pressing. Jung posits that we have lost religious faith and have nothing left but our minds (a rather existentialist premise). So we must know our minds better. We must ask what our minds can do, and have already done; how we think, along what prescribed or predetermined lines. This is also why, in our times, a science of mind has belatedly sprung up, or is finally sought for, as never in any age before us.

Man is a conglomerate of superstitions, both historical and contemporary. Today, in order for him to know himself, he must strip away centuries of intellectual errors and lingering confusions. A study of his myths in almost every branch of knowledge is a plausible first step in making a psychological study of man's whole structure of thought.

IX

Considerably earlier than Jung, as we have said, Adolf Bastian propounded the theory of "elemental ideas." The unanimity of myths is the result of an inherently uniform disposition of the human mind. When the mind has certain ideas, it will express them—within fixed limits—in identical ways *always* and *everywhere*. Seizing on this theory, Adolf Bauer argued that it accounts for the sameness of the qualities which the Culture Hero takes on wherever he appears in primitive stories.

Very recently, Kilton Stewart—an anthropologist—has stated his conviction that all men develop according to a single mental pattern. He claims to have validated his concept by tests and observations amongst the native tribes of Luzon in the Philippines. "This single pattern can be discovered by a psychological study of successive levels of humans, ranging from the primitive to the sophisticate."

Other aspects of this are discussed by Alexander Lindey, who comments: "Identical archetypes can be found in simple tales from the South Seas and in the sophisticated pages of Ovid's *Metamorphoses*. The Arabian Nights did not reach Europe until the eighteenth century; yet there are many intimations of it in Celtic and Scandinavian folklore. The artifacts of all primitive cultures reveal certain common decorative motifs (the zigzag, the checker, the spiral, the scroll) and common forms. These flow from similarity in function, materials and tools, not from copying. For example, a strong kinship in design—but no discoverable link—exists between the decorated pottery of ancient Persia (going back as far as 3500 B.C.) and that of American Indians."

But Carl Jung and his followers are still the outstanding advocates of this belief. A thorough analysis of a particular figure in a dream or myth, declares Jung, could demonstrate easily that it is an archetypal picture such as can be reproduced over and over again in any age and any place. We might say that the large categories of creation myths—including the scientific theories—are also, in the Jungian sense of the word, archetypal pictures. We might also go along with Jung in believing that, to some extent at least, they are involuntary revelations of a psychic, but unconscious, precondition. This is really a logical conclusion regarding the creation myths, and regarding astrophysical thinking, too. Something similar to a group of primordial images exists in our minds. We might not pretend to know what it is, but the reader has been shown how much evidence there is of it.

To this one must add that one need not say that the rather rigid way in which we see the world—the predestined or preordained way—is ever a true picture of it. It is merely a limit of our mind or senses or habit of thinking. We can leave out all mysticism in our exposition of this. But at the same time, it is equally possible that this way of seeing the world—in primordial images of one kind or another—is a true insight. Just as there is no good reason to think it is, there is no good reason to think it is not. There may be no physical authenticity to our mythical vision of the universe, but for us there is at least a psychological one.

Kerényi expresses very well the peculiarity of the mythical process—which I feel it is important to clarify—as it was experienced by early man: "Behind the 'Why?' stands the 'Whence?' More strictly still, there is no initial question at all in mythology any more than there is in archaic Greek philosophy, nothing but the direct unquestioning return to the primal state or substance, a spontaneous regression to the 'ground'. . . . The philosopher tries to pierce through the world of appearances in order to say what 'really is,' but the teller of myths steps back into primordiality in order to tell us what 'originally was.' Primordiality is the same thing for him as authenticity. Without venturing to say whether this results in real authenticity, the true immediacy of subject and object, this procedure gives us some idea of mythological authority or substantiation." Kerényi states, elsewhere, that the tales never indicate "causes" but only primary substances that never age, can never be surpassed, and produce everything always. "They form the ground or formation of the world, since everything rests on them. . . . The mythologies speak . . . of the coming-to-be of the divine cosmos or a universal God. Birth and sunrise merely endow that universal beginning with physical features and a sort of golden haze."

Certainly it is significant, though hardly a final "proof," that the primordial image most common and vivid to all manner of men—from ancient Sumerian to contemporary yet naked Polynesian—is that of God or some kind of divinity.

If our thinking is preordained, how can we say, as we did

a few pages ago, that much free play of the imagination is found in myth? This is possible; there is room for both in the elaborate structure of most myths. We might be persuaded that there is an area of free association of ideas. Our emphasis here is on the word "association." But there is another area where man's intellect obeys an unknown *Diktat.* To repeat what was said earlier in this essay, we do not think as we wish, but as we must. The freedom of man's thought is essentially an illusion.

INDEX